25 All-Time Big Rock G━━━━s

Part One
Rock Anthems

Addicted To Love Robert Palmer

All Right Now Free

Behind The Mask Eric Clapton

Brothers In Arms Dire Straits

Don't You (Forget About Me) Simple Minds

Gimme All Your Lovin' ZZ Top

Goldfinger Ash

I Found Someone Cher

In The Air Tonight Phil Collins

Pinball Wizard The Who

School's Out Alice Cooper

The Changingman Paul Weller

The Final Countdown Europe

Part Two
90's Rock Guitar

A Design For Life Manic Street Preachers

Blinded By The Sun The Seahorses

D'You Know What I Mean Oasis

Hand In My Pocket Alanis Morissette

If God Will Send His Angels U2

Keep The Faith Bon Jovi

Local Boy In The Photograph Stereophonics

Sorted For E's And Wizz Pulp

Ten Storey Love Song The Stone Roses

The Changingman Paul Weller

The Riverboat Song Ocean Colour Scene

Wide Open Space Mansun

Zombie The Cranberries

WISE PUBLICATIONS
London/New York/Paris/Sydney/Copenhagen/Berlin/Madrid/Tokyo

Exclusive distributors:

Music Sales Limited

8/9 Frith Street, London W1D 3JB, England.

Music Sales Pty Limited

120 Rothschild Avenue, Rosebery, NSW 2018, Australia.

Order No.AM972873

ISBN 0-7119-9216-9

This book © Copyright 2002 by Wise Publications.

Cover design by Hilite Design.
Photographs courtesy of Rex Features.

Printed in the United Kingdom by Printwise (Haverhill) Limited, Haverhill, Suffolk.

Your Guarantee of Quality:
As publishers, we strive to produce every book to the highest commercial standards.
This book has been carefully designed to minimise awkward page turns
and to make playing from it a real pleasure.
Particular care has been given to specifying acid-free, neutral-sized
paper made from pulps which have not been elemental chlorine bleached.
This pulp is from farmed sustainable forests and was produced with special regard for the environment.
Throughout, the printing and binding have been planned to ensure a sturdy,
attractive publication which should give years of enjoyment.
If your copy fails to meet our high standards, please inform us and we will gladly replace it.

Music Sales' complete catalogue describes thousands of titles and is
available in full colour sections by subject, direct from Music Sales Limited.
Please state your areas of interest and send a cheque/postal order for £1.50 for postage to:
Music Sales Limited, Newmarket Road, Bury St. Edmunds, Suffolk IP33 3YB.

www.musicsales.com

Guitar
Tab

Guitar Tablature Explained

Guitar music can be noted three different ways: on a musical stave, in tablature, and in rhythm slashes.

RHYTHM SLASHES are written above the stave. Strum chords in the rhythm indicated. Round noteheads indicate single notes.

THE MUSICAL STAVE shows pitches and rhythms and is divided by lines into bars. Pitches are named after the first seven letters of the alphabet.

TABLATURE graphically represents the guitar fingerboard. Each horizontal line represents a string, and each number represents a fret.

4th string, 2nd fret   1st & 2nd strings open, played together   open D chord

definitions for special guitar notation

SEMI-TONE BEND: Strike the note and bend up a semi-tone (1/2 step).

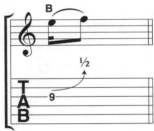

WHOLE-TONE BEND: Strike the note and bend up a whole-tone (whole step).

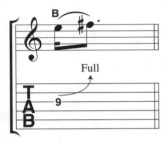

GRACE NOTE BEND: Strike the note and bend as indicated. Play the first note as quickly as possible.

QUARTER-TONE BEND: Strike the note and bend up a 1/4 step.

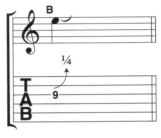

BEND & RELEASE: Strike the note and bend up as indicated, then release back to the original note.

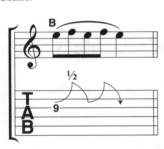

COMPOUND BEND & RELEASE: Strike the note and bend up and down in the rhythm indicated.

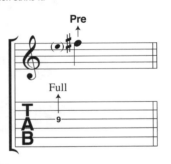

PRE-BEND: Bend the note as indicated, then strike it.

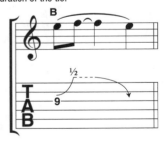

PRE-BEND & RELEASE: Bend the note as indicated. Strike it and release the note back to the original pitch.

UNISON BEND: Strike the two notes simultaneously and bend the lower note up to the pitch of the higher.

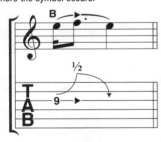

BEND & RESTRIKE: Strike the note and bend as indicated then restrike the string where the symbol occurs.

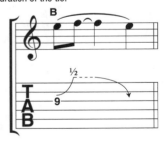

BEND, HOLD AND RELEASE: Same as bend and release but hold the bend for the duration of the tie.

BEND AND TAP: Bend the note as indicated and tap the higher fret while still holding the bend.

VIBRATO: The string is vibrated by rapidly bending and releasing the note with the fretting hand.

HAMMER-ON: Strike the first (lower) note with one finger, then sound the higher note (on the same string) with another finger by fretting it without picking.

PULL-OFF: Place both fingers on the notes to be sounded, Strike the first note and without picking, pull the finger off to sound the second (lower) note.

LEGATO SLIDE (GLISS): Strike the first note and then slide the same fret-hand finger up or down to the second note. The second note is not struck.

NOTE: The speed of any bend is indicated by the music notation and tempo.

SHIFT SLIDE (GLISS & RESTRIKE): Same as legato slide, except the second note is struck.

TRILL: Very rapidly alternate between the notes indicated by continuously hammering on and pulling off.

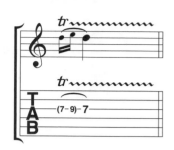

TAPPING: Hammer ("tap") the fret indicated with the pick-hand index or middle finger and pull off to the note fretted by the fret hand.

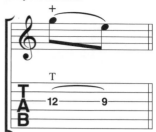

PICK SCRAPE: The edge of the pick is rubbed down (or up) the string, producing a scratchy sound.

MUFFLED STRINGS: A percussive sound is produced by laying the fret hand across the string(s) without depressing, and striking them with the pick hand.

NATURAL HARMONIC: Strike the note while the fret-hand lightly touches the string directly over the fret indicated.

PINCH HARMONIC: The note is fretted normally and a harmonic is produced by adding the edge of the thumb or the tip of the index finger of the pick hand to the normal pick attack.

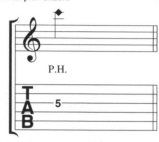

HARP HARMONIC: The note is fretted normally and a harmonic is produced by gently resting the pick hand's index finger directly above the indicated fret (in parentheses) while the pick hand's thumb or pick assists by plucking the appropriate string.

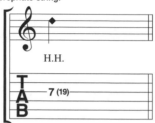

PALM MUTING: The note is partially muted by the pick hand lightly touching the string(s) just before the bridge.

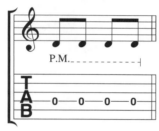

RAKE: Drag the pick across the strings indicated with a single motion.

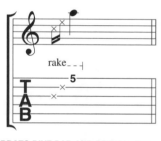

TREMOLO PICKING: The note is picked as rapidly and continuously as possible.

ARPEGGIATE: Play the notes of the chord indicated by quickly rolling them from bottom to top.

SWEEP PICKING: Rhythmic downstroke and/or upstroke motion across the strings.

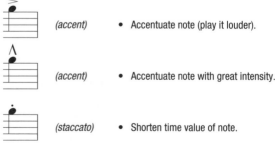

VIBRATO DIVE BAR AND RETURN: The pitch of the note or chord is dropped a specific number of steps (in rhythm) then returned to the original pitch.

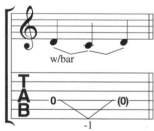

VIBRATO BAR SCOOP: Depress the bar just before striking the note, then quickly release the bar.

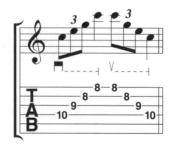

VIBRATO BAR DIP: Strike the note and then immediately drop a specific number of steps, then release back to the original pitch.

additional musical definitions

$>$ (accent)	•	Accentuate note (play it louder).
$\wedge$ (accent)	•	Accentuate note with great intensity.
• (staccato)	•	Shorten time value of note.
⊓	•	Downstroke
V	•	Upstroke

D.%. al Coda

D.C. al Fine

tacet

1. **2.**

- Go back to the sign (%), then play until the bar marked *To Coda* ⊕ then skip to the section marked ⊕ *Coda*.
- Go back to the beginning of the song and play until the bar marked *Fine* (end).
- Instrument is silent (drops out).
- Repeat bars between signs.
- When a repeated section has different endings, play the first ending only the first time and the second ending only the second time.

NOTE: Tablature numbers in parentheses mean: 1. The note is sustained, but a new articulation (such as hammer on or slide) begins.
2. A note may be fretted but not necessarily played.

All Right Now

Words & Music by Paul Rodgers & Andy Fraser

7

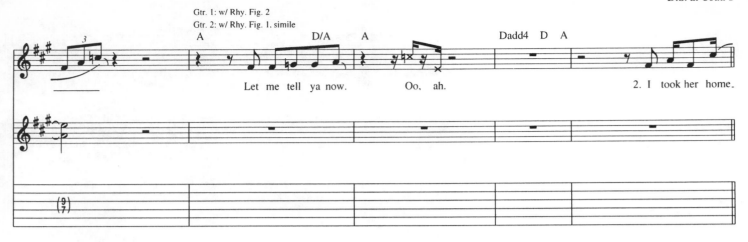

Coda 1

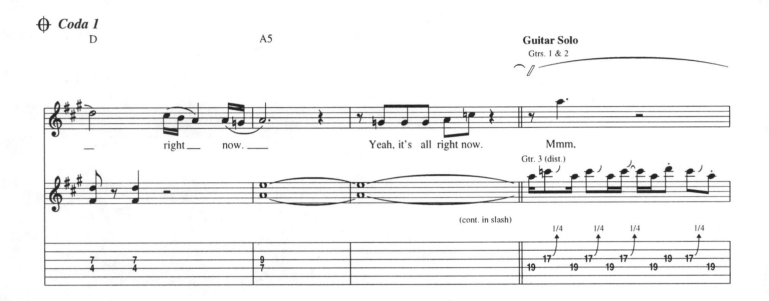

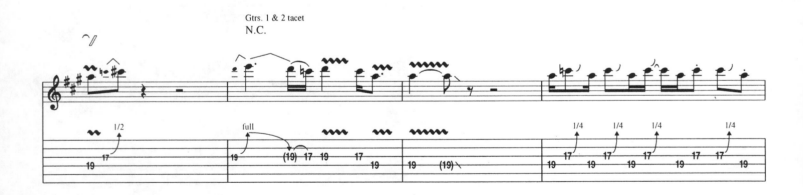

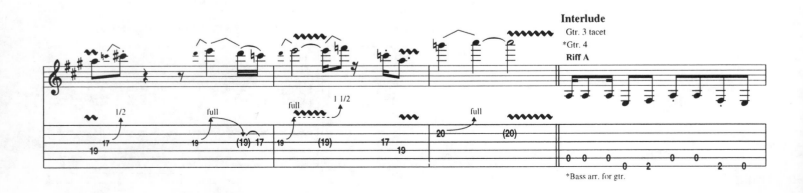

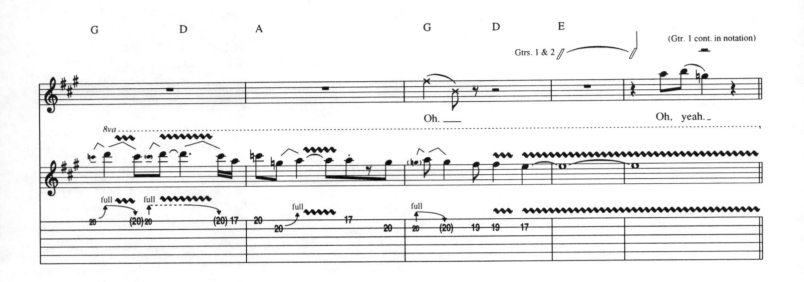

Bridge

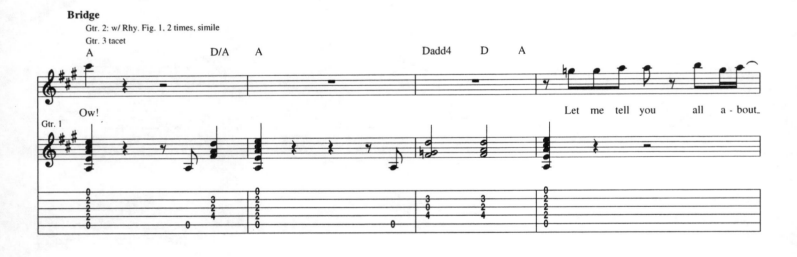

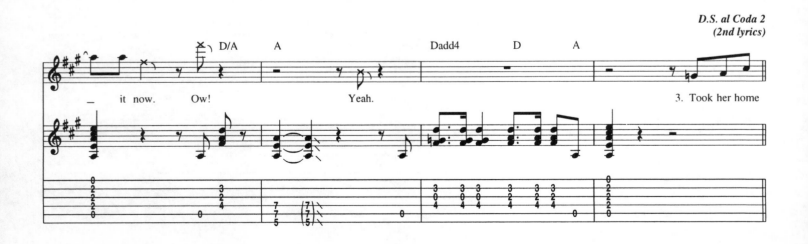

Addicted To Love

Words & Music by Robert Palmer

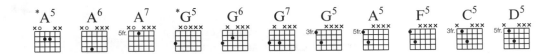

* Keyboards arr. for Gtr.

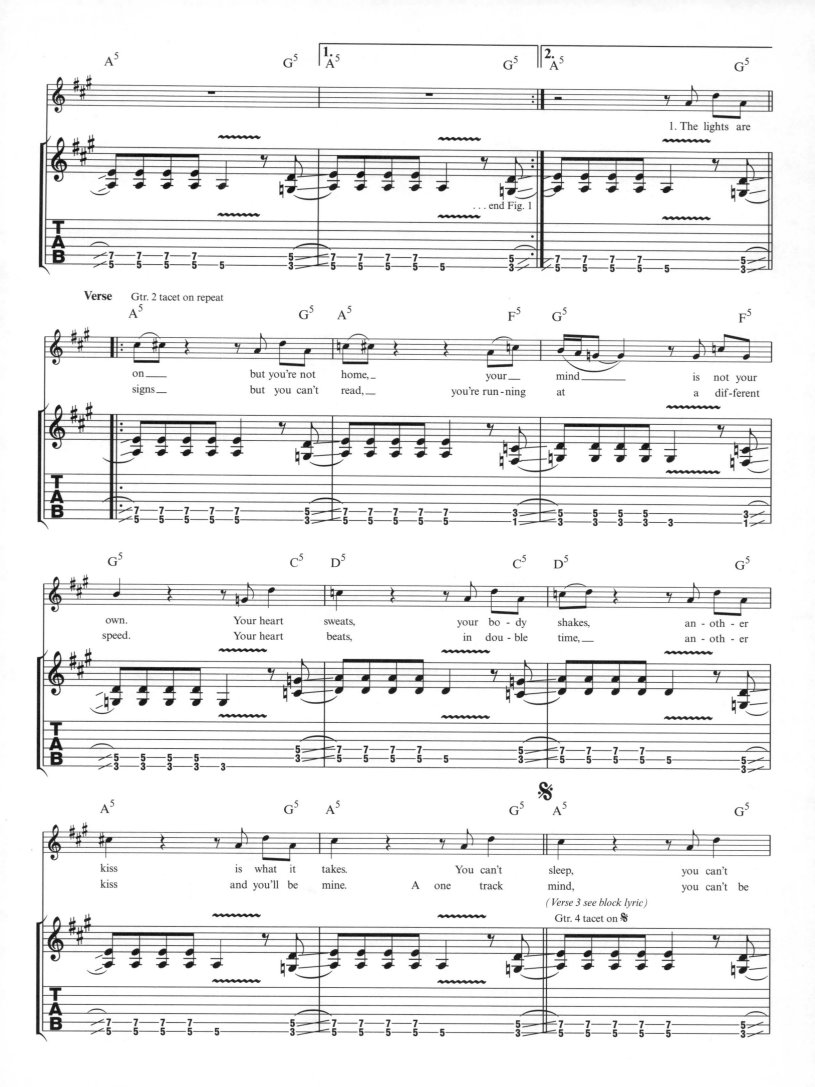

Verse 3:

The lights are on, but you're not home
Your will is not your own
Your heart sweats, your teeth grind
Another kiss and you'll be mine.

16

Behind The Mask

Words & Music by Ryuichi Sakomoto, Chris Mosdell & Michael Jackson

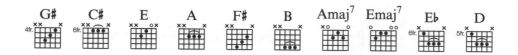

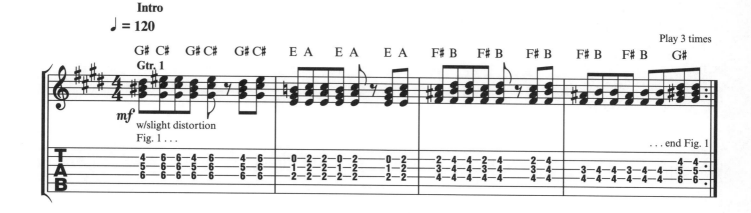

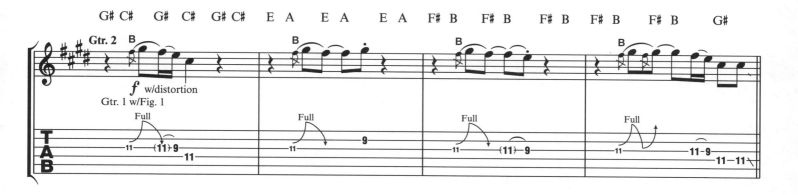

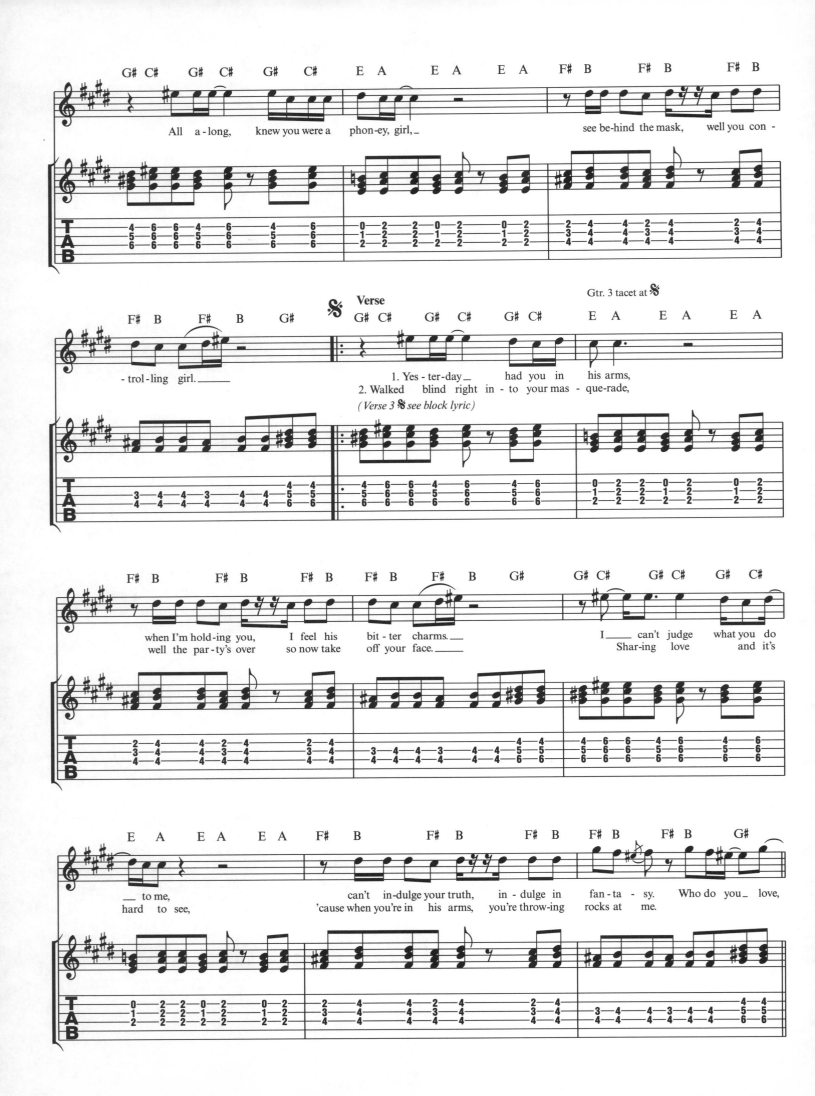

18

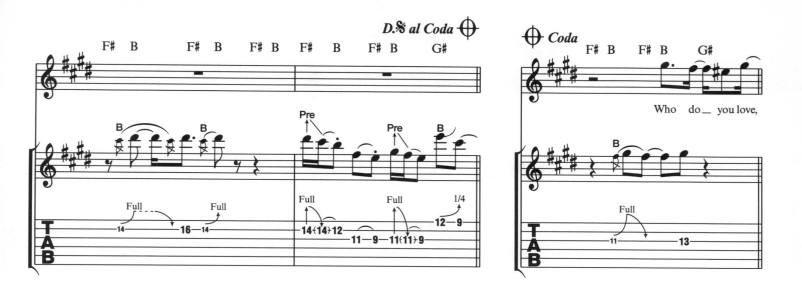

Verse 3 (𝄋):

I walked around suffering in my doom
When I come to you, you're sitting in your room
The truth in you, I have longed to trace
To take off the mask so I can see your face.

Brothers In Arms

Words & Music by Mark Knopfler

23

24

Don't You (Forget About Me)

Words & Music by Keith Forsey & Steve Schiff

28

* Keyboard arr. for Gtr.

don't ___ you ___ for-get a-bout me. ___

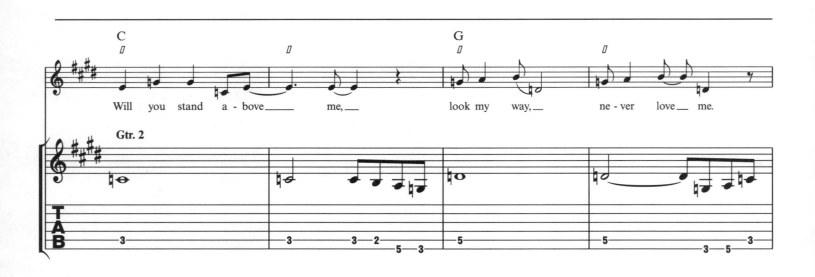

Will you stand a-bove ___ me, ___ look my way, ___ ne-ver love ___ me.

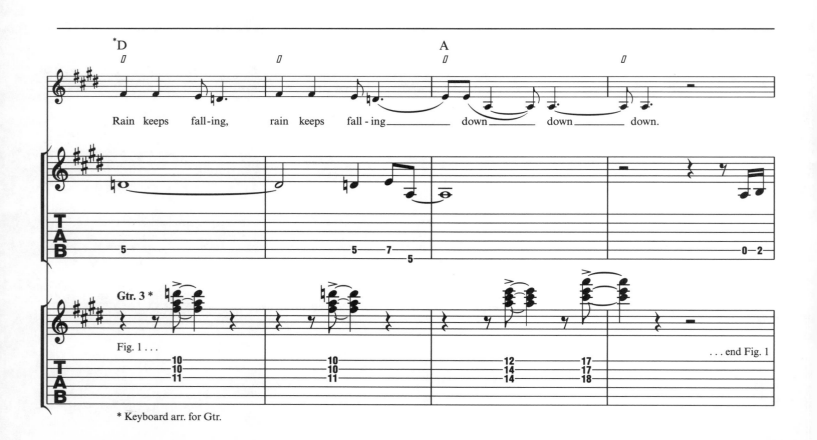

Rain keeps fall-ing, rain keeps fall-ing ___ down ___ down ___ down.

Fig. 1 . . .   . . . end Fig. 1

* Keyboard arr. for Gtr.

Will you re-cog-nise me, call my name or walk on by.

Rain keeps fall-ing, rain keeps fall-ing down down down down.

Gtr. 3 w/Fig. 1

As you walk on by will you call my name,

Gtr. 4 *

* Keyboard arr. for Gtr.

as you walk on by will you call my name.

When you walk a-way,____

oh, will you walk a-way,____ oh, will you walk a-way.

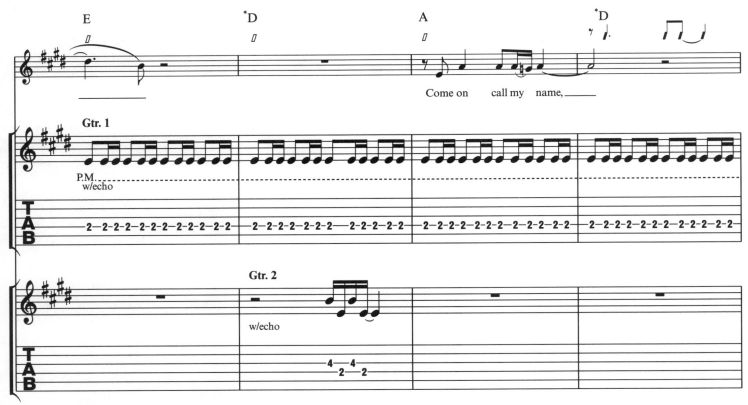

Come on call my name,____

Gtr. 1

P.M.
w/echo

Gtr. 2

w/echo

will you___ call   my_____ name.   I sing,

Gtrs. 1 & 2

La   la la la la_____   la la la la_____   la la la   la la la la la la

Gtr. 3 *

* Keyboard arr. for Gtr.

la   la la la la_____   la la la la_____   la la la   la la la la la la

Repeat ad lib. to fade

The Changingman

Words & Music by Paul Weller & Brendan Lynch

36

The Final Countdown

Words & Music by Joey Tempest

* Keyboard arr. for Gtr.

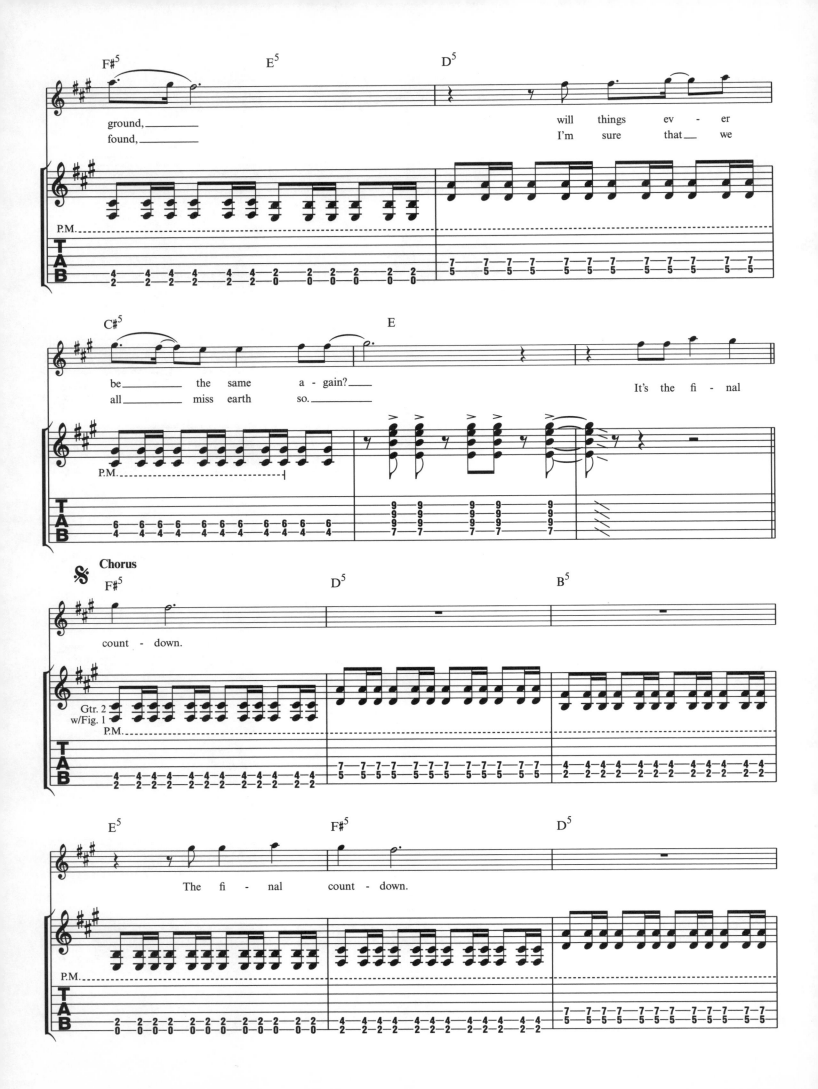

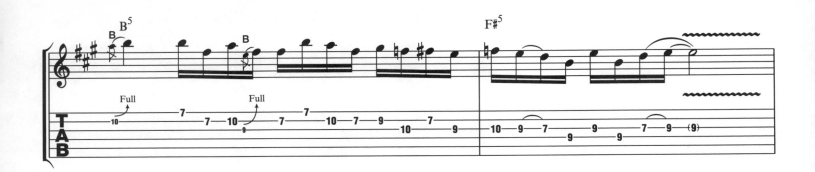

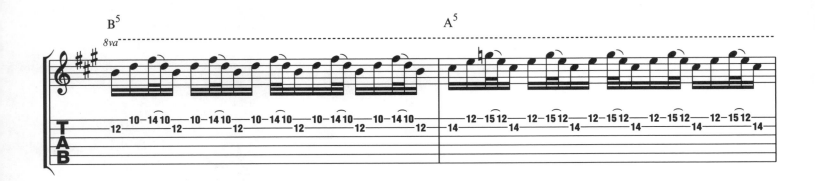

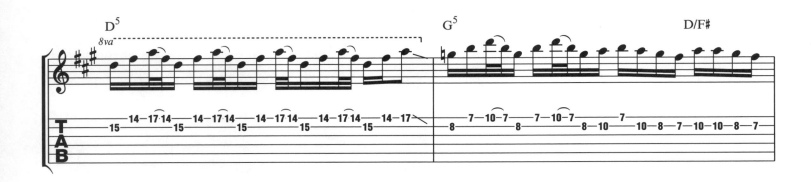

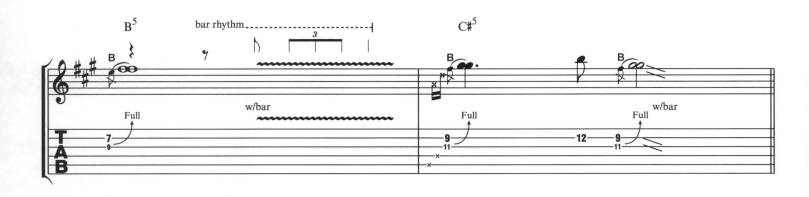

Gimme All Your Lovin'

Words & Music by Billy Gibbons, Dusty Hill & Frank Beard

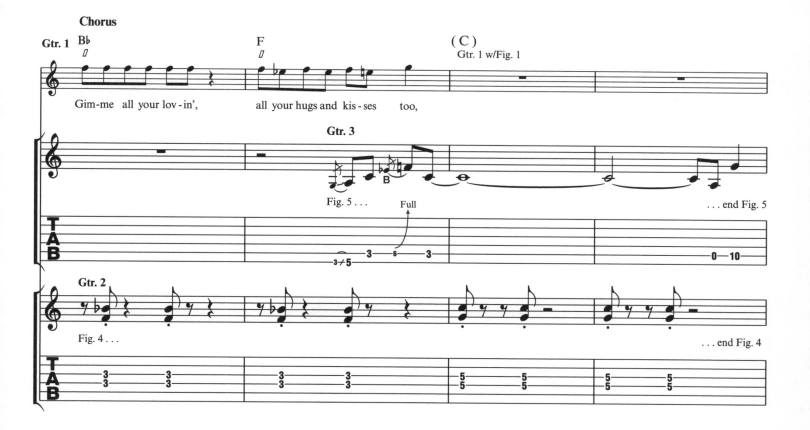

gim-me all your lov-in',_____ don't let up un-til we're through._____

2. You got to

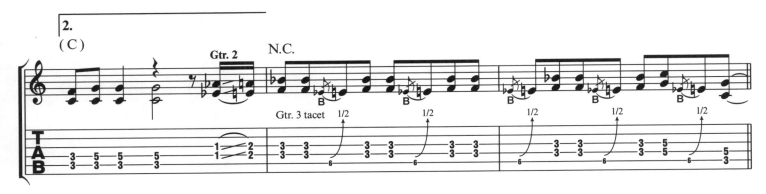

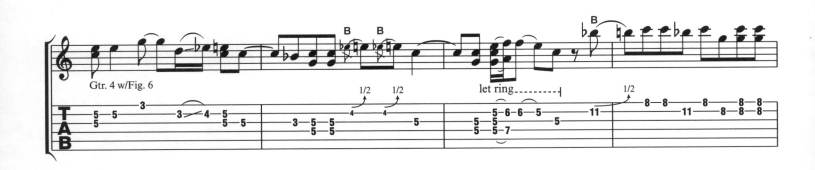

49

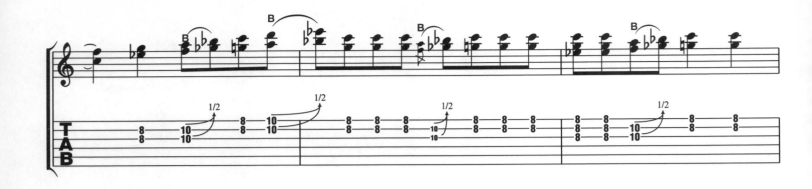

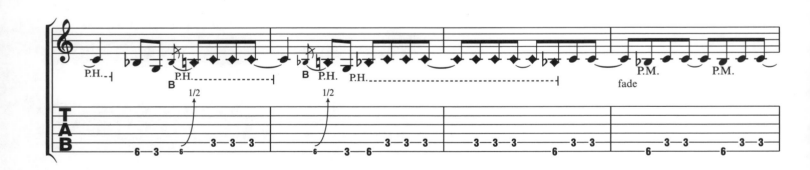

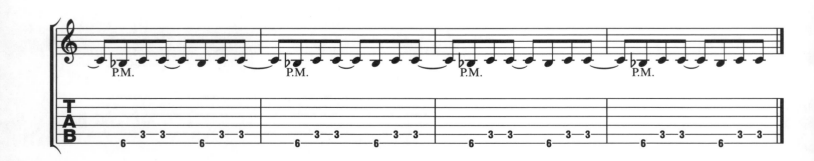

Goldfinger

Words & Music by Tim Wheeler

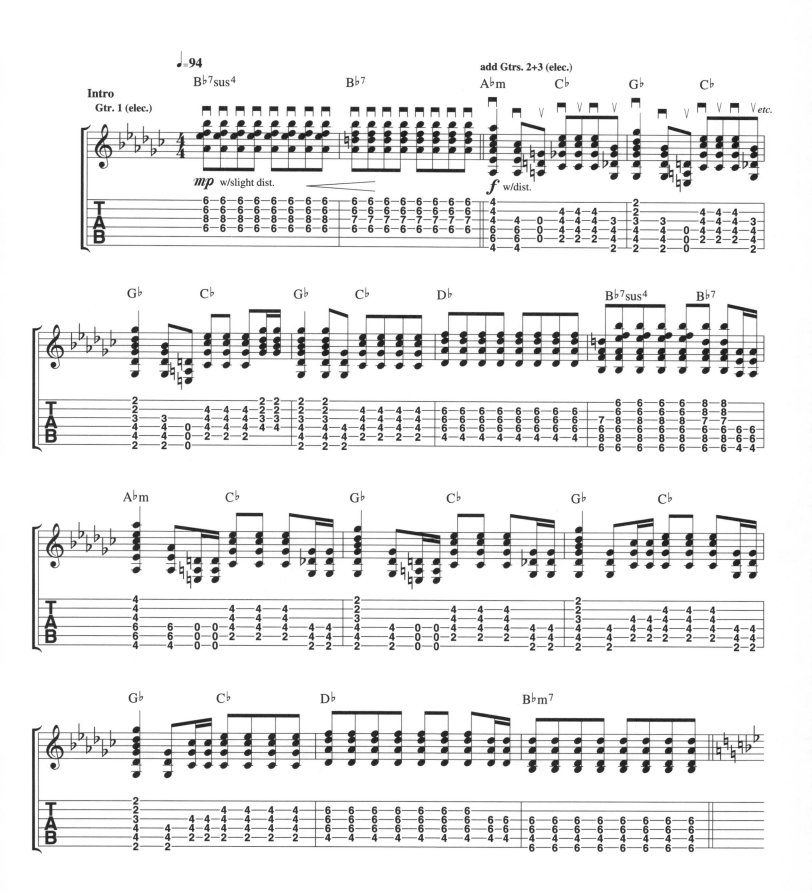

55

I Found Someone

Words & Music by Michael Bolton & Mark Mangold

In The Air Tonight

Words & Music by Phil Collins

63

Pinball Wizard

Words & Music by Peter Townshend

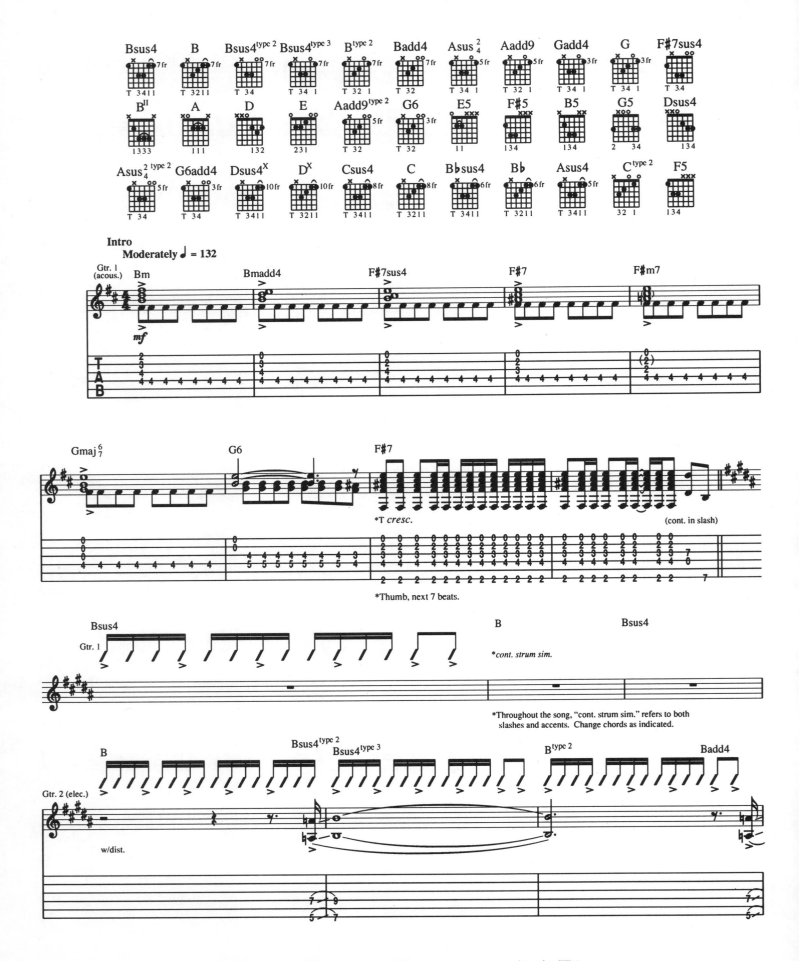

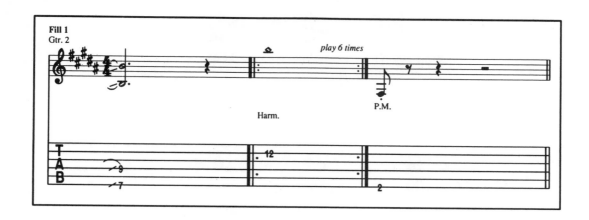

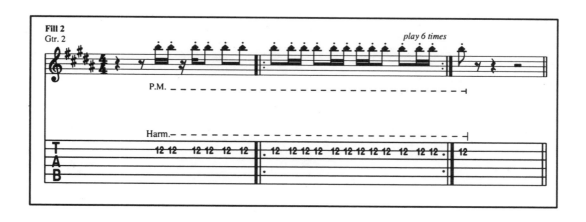

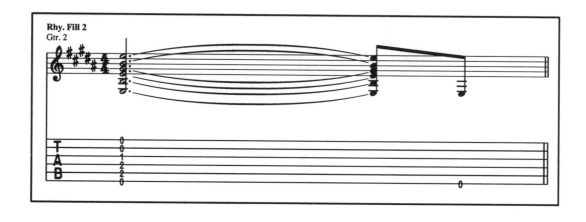

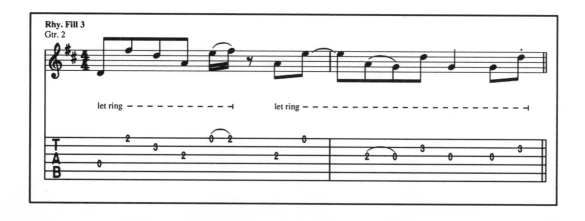

School's Out

Words & Music by Alice Cooper & Michael Bruce

Part Two
90's Rock Guitar

Guitar Tab

A DESIGN FOR LIFE

Music by James Dean Bradfield & Sean Moore
Lyrics by Nicky Wire

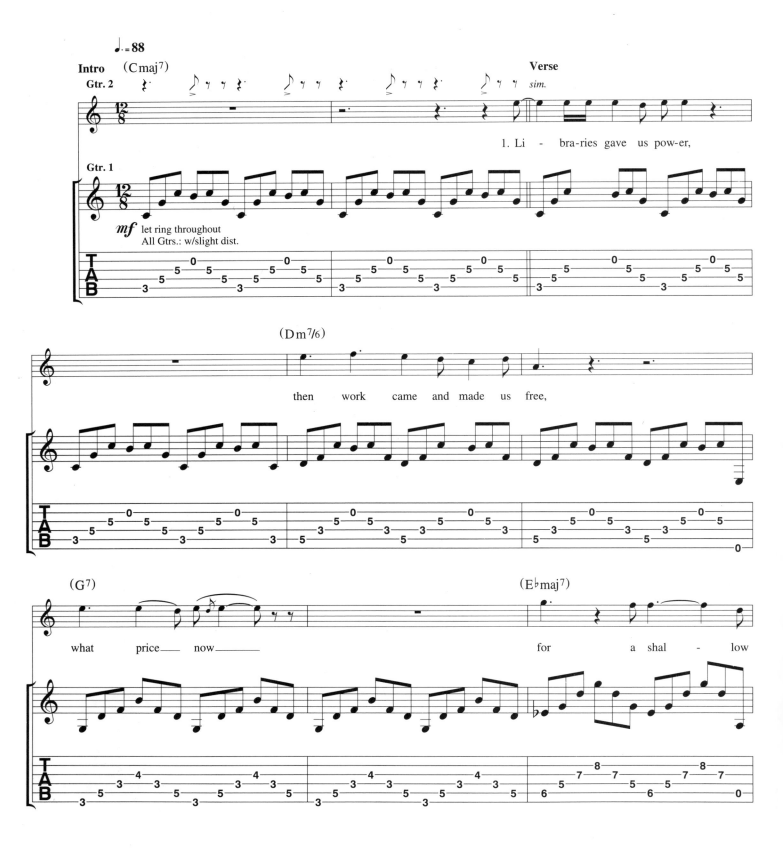

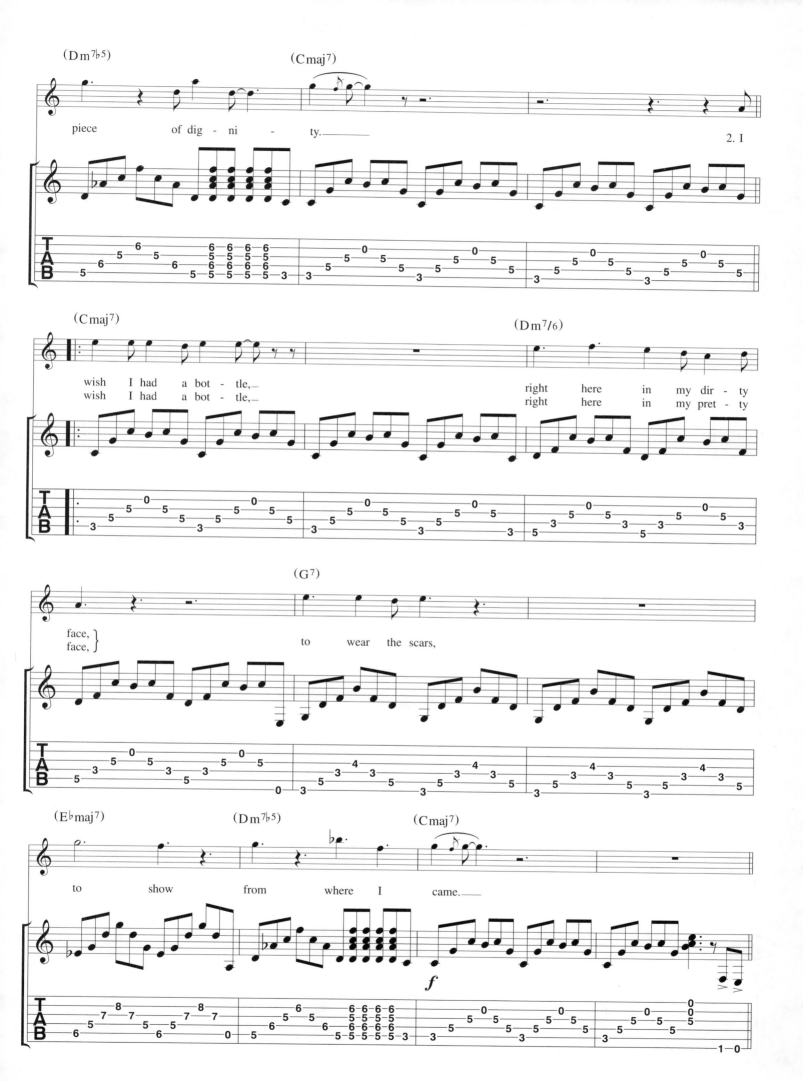

9

BLINDED BY THE SUN

Words & Music by Chris Helme

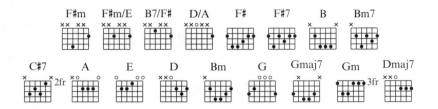

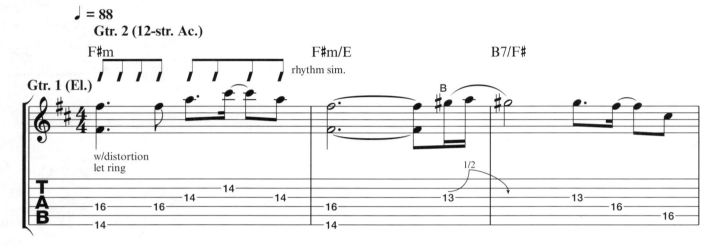

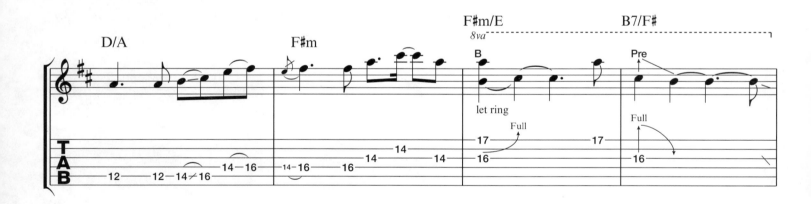

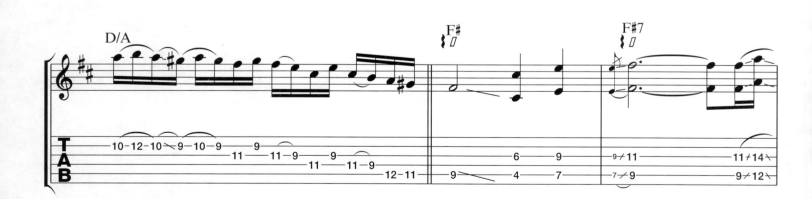

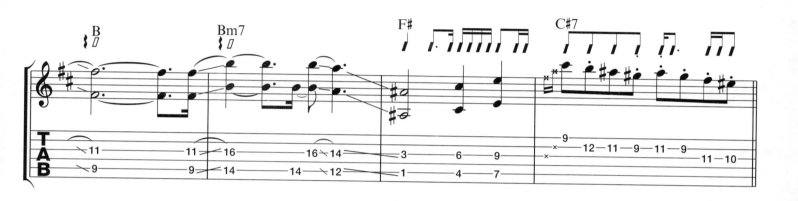

Verse

How would you feel__ if I_____ was to kneel right down__ at your feet?_____ Right now

is the way__ it's go - ing to be,__ from now un - til for-ev - er. Let's have

less of get-ting cle-ver with me.

Verse

Gtr. 3. tacet on repeat

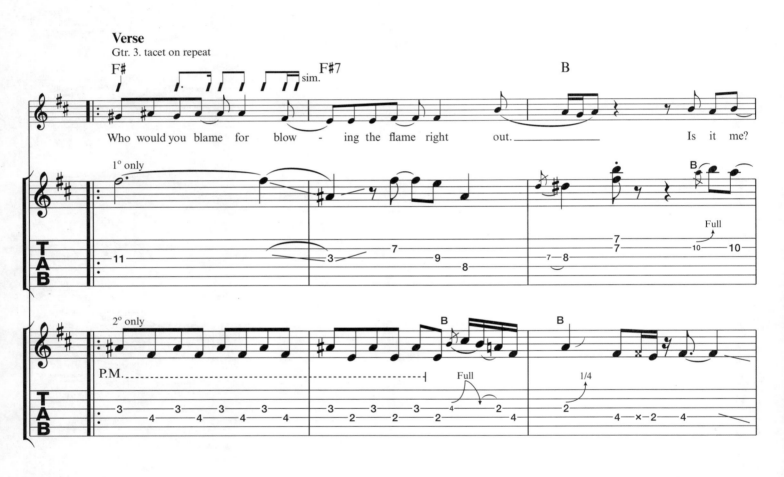

Who would you blame for blow - ing the flame right out. _____ Is it me?

There is no doubt _____ I can do _____ what I _____

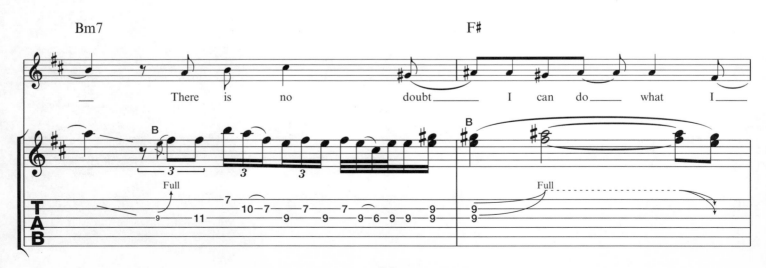

13

D'YOU KNOW WHAT I MEAN

Words & Music by Noel Gallagher

* Symbols in parentheses represent chord names with respect to capoed gtr (Tab 0 = 2nd fret)
Symbols above represent actual sounding chords.

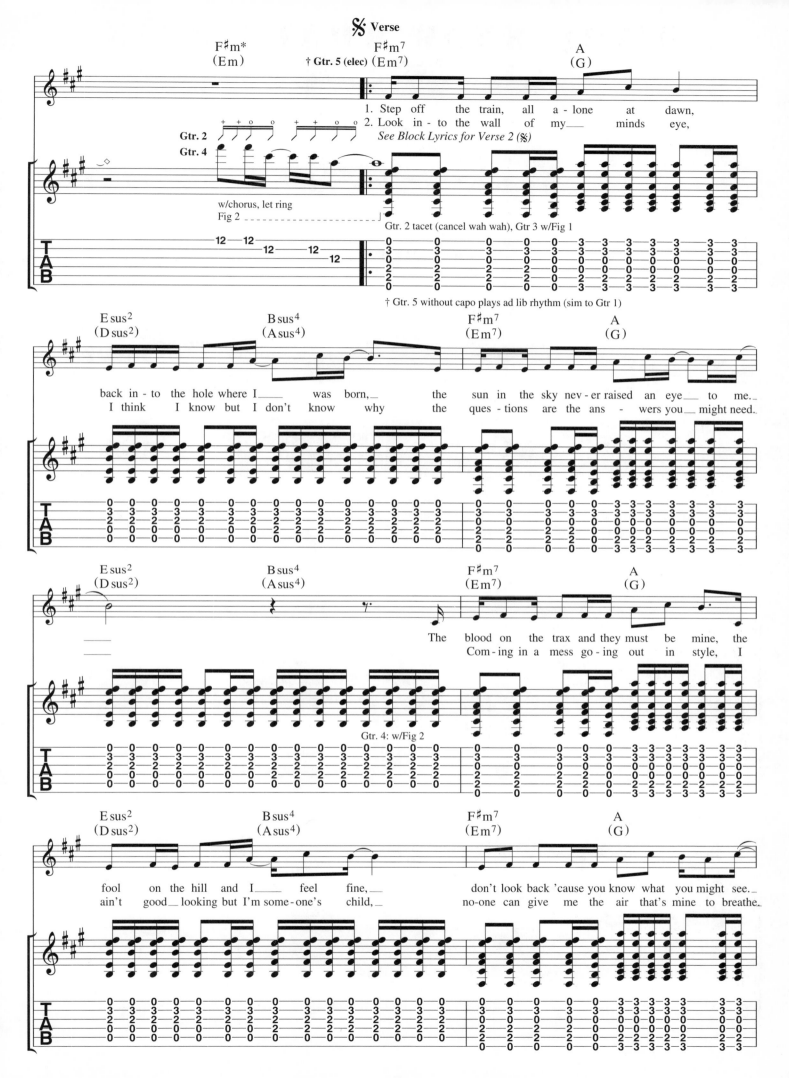

17

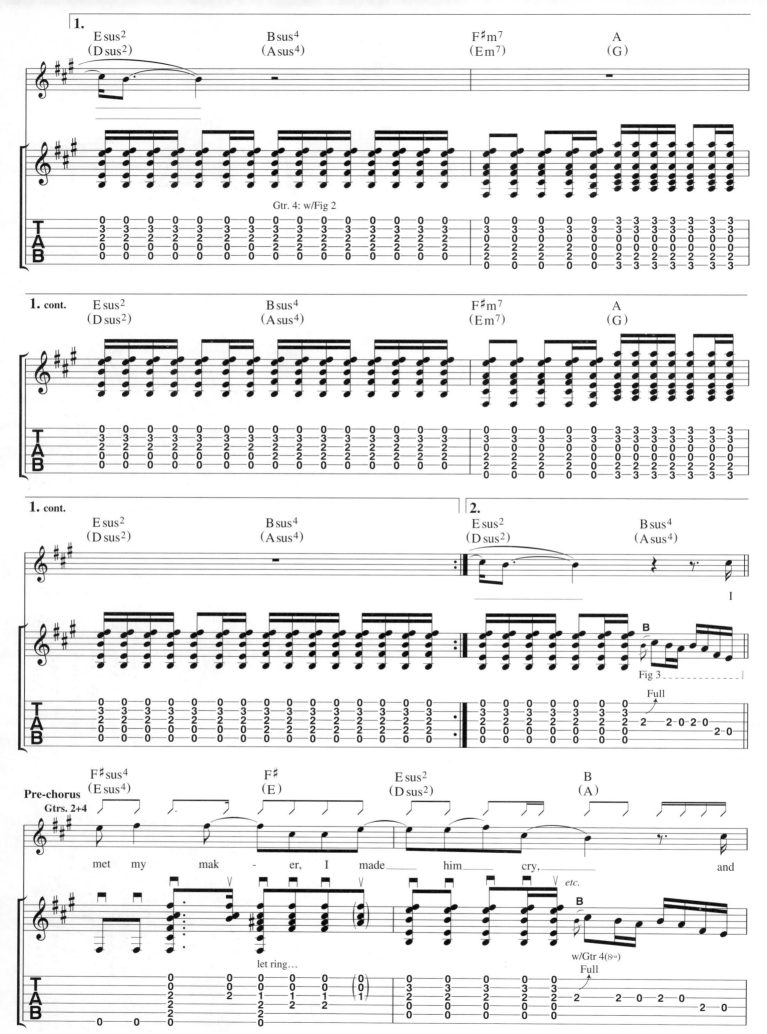

Gtr. 4 continues sim to Gtr. 1 but plays Fig 3 an octave (12 frets) higher

20

21

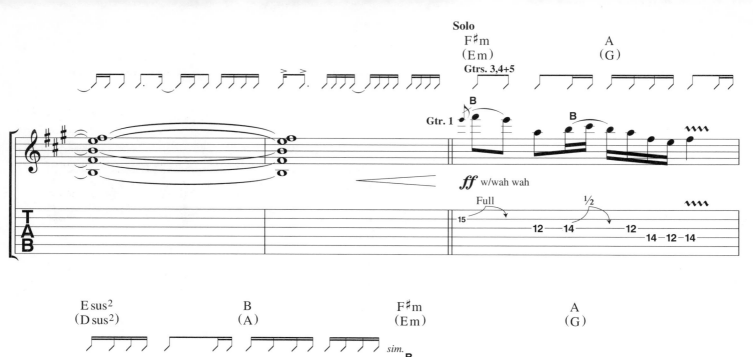

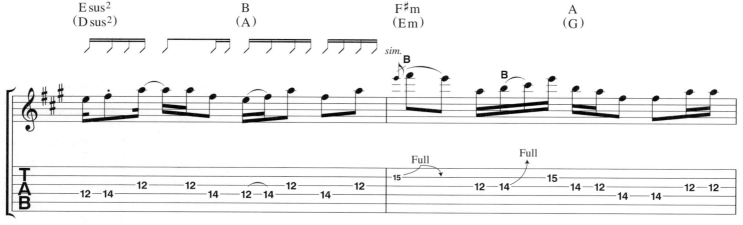

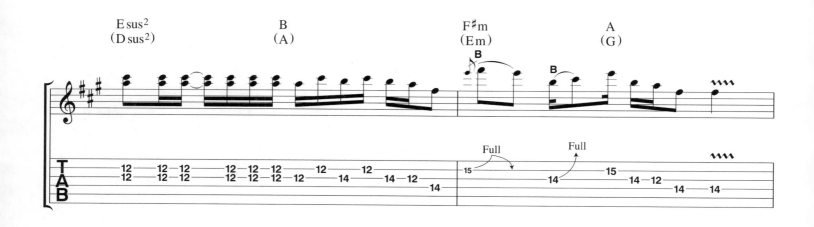

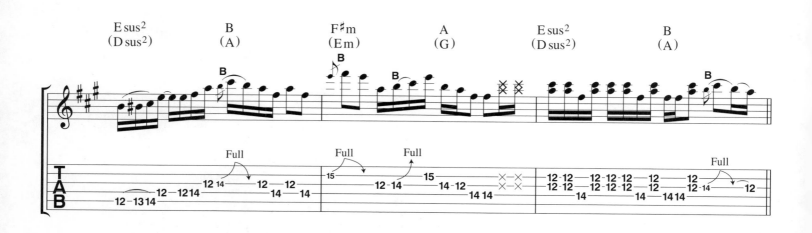

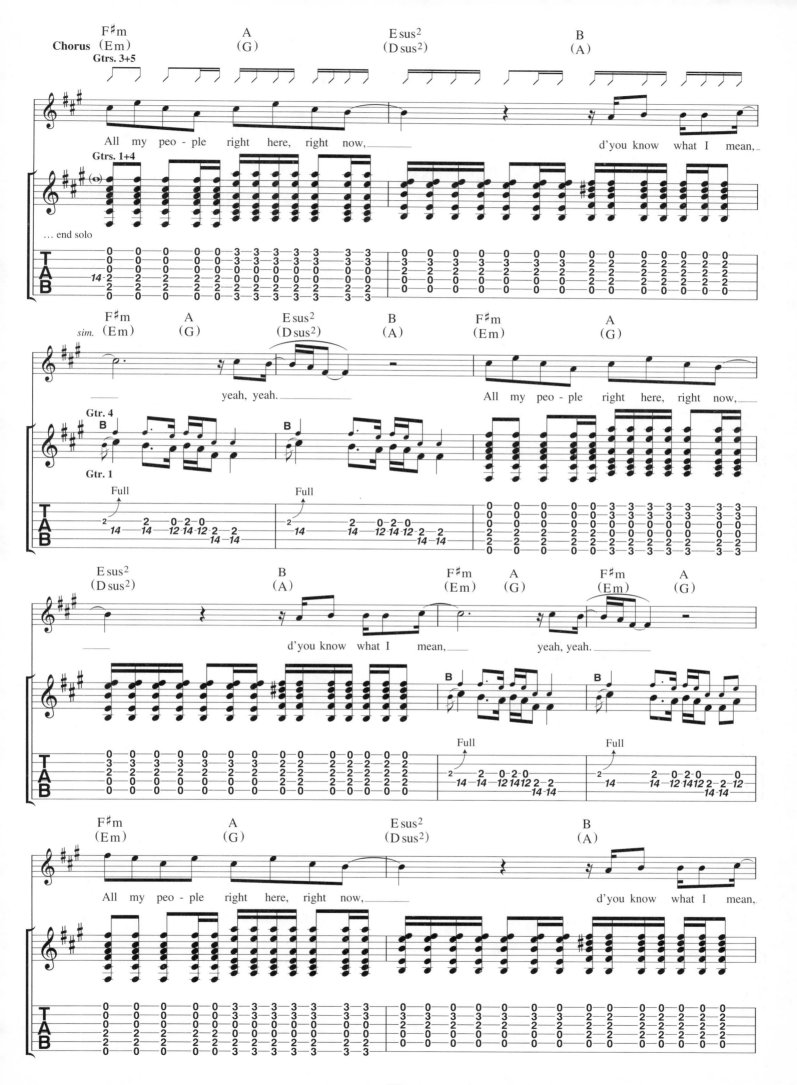

Verse 3:
I don't really care for what you believe
So open up your fist or you won't receive
The thoughts and the words of everyman you'll need.
So get up off the floor and believe in life
No one's ever gonna ever ask you twice
Get on the bus and bring it on home to me.

HAND IN MY POCKET

Words & Music by Alanis Morissette & Glen Ballard

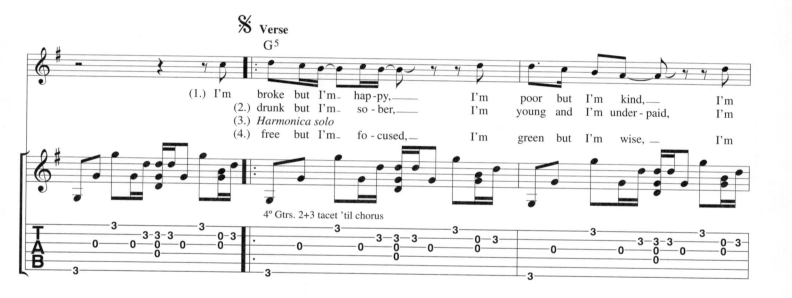

26

IF GOD WILL SEND HIS ANGELS

Music by U2
Lyrics by Bono & The Edge

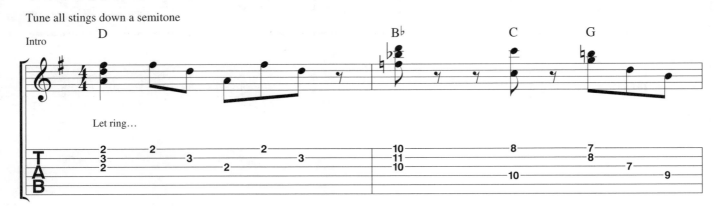

1. No - bo - dy else___ here___ ba - by,___ no - one here___ to blame,___
2. No - bo - dy made___ you do it, no - one put words___ in your mouth___
3. Je - sus nev - er let me down,___ you know Je - sus used to show me the score,___

no - one to point the fin - ger it's just
no - bo - dy here tak - ing or - ders when love
then they put Je - sus in show busi - ness now it's

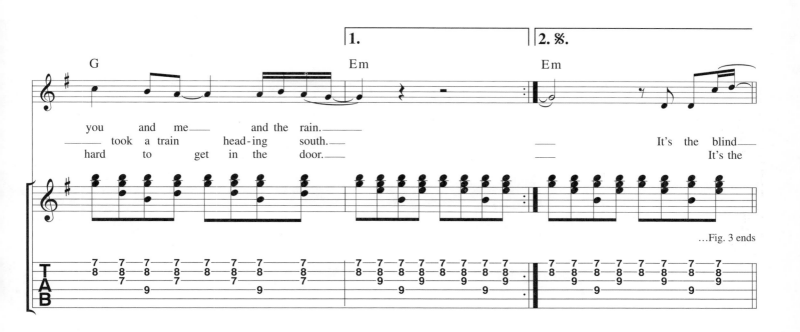

you and me and the rain.
took a train head - ing south.
hard to get in the door.

It's the blind
It's the

...Fig. 3 ends

Pre-chorus

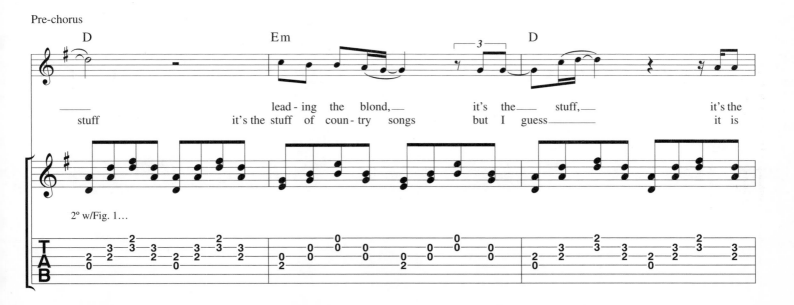

stuff lead - ing the blond, it's the stuff, it's the
it's the stuff of coun - try songs but I guess it is

2° w/Fig. 1...

31

33

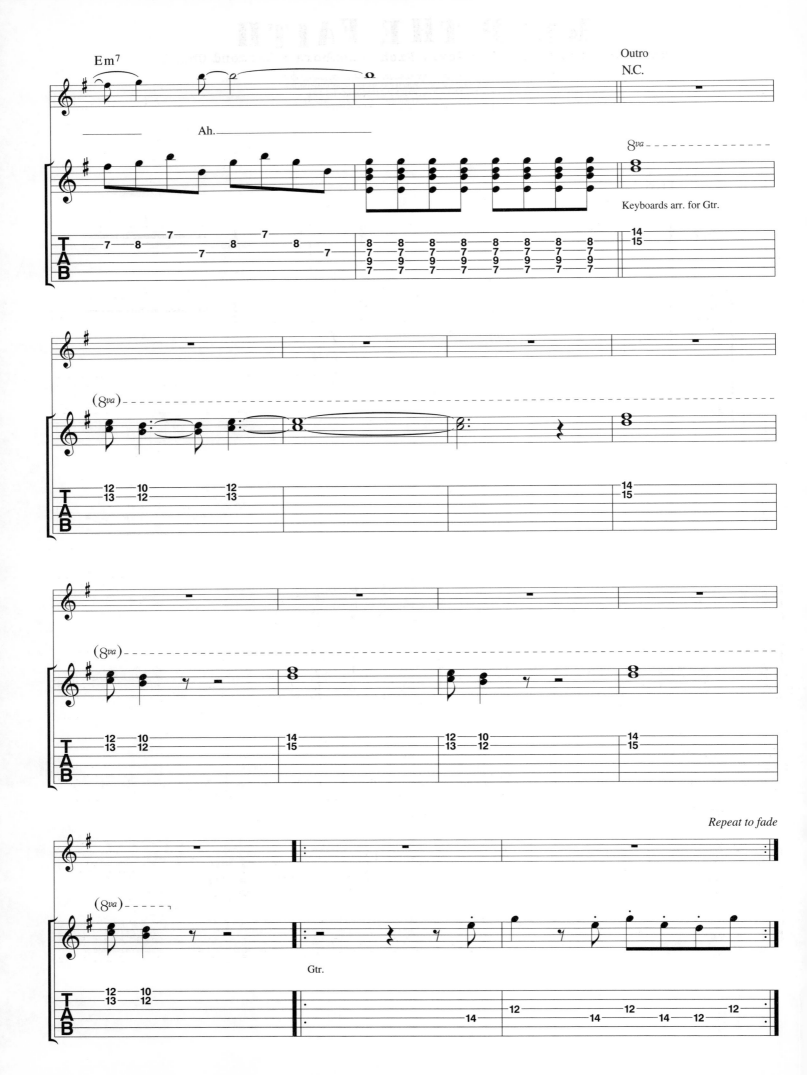

KEEP THE FAITH

Words & Music by Jon Bon Jovi, Richie Sambora & Desmond Child

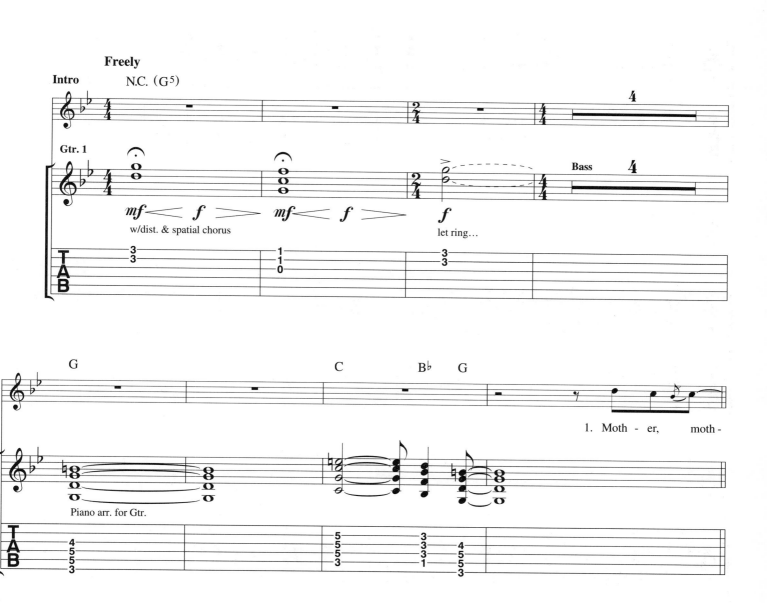

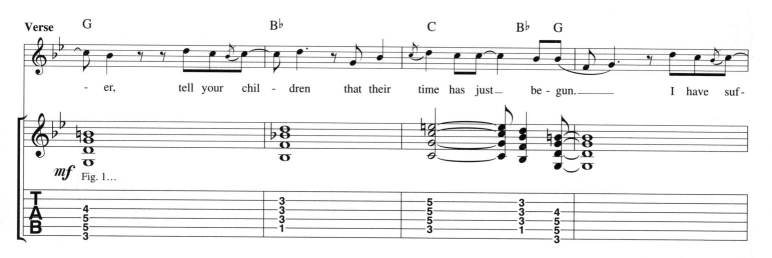

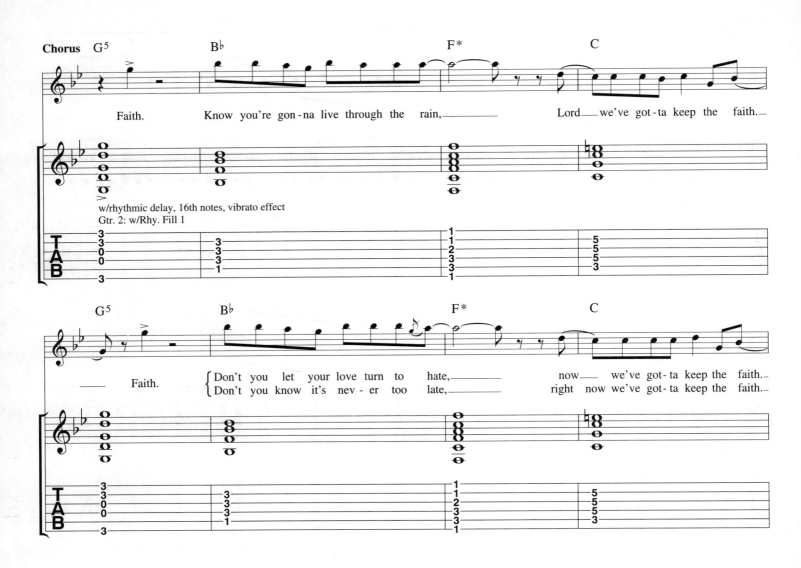

Chorus

Faith.

Know you're gon‑na live through the rain,_____ Lord_____ we've got‑ta keep the faith._____

w/rhythmic delay, 16th notes, vibrato effect
Gtr. 2: w/Rhy. Fill 1

_____ Faith.

Don't you let your love turn to hate,_____ now_____ we've got‑ta keep the faith._____
Don't you know it's nev‑er too late,_____ right now we've got‑ta keep the faith._____

Rhy. Fill 1

Gtr. 2

w/slight dist./delay

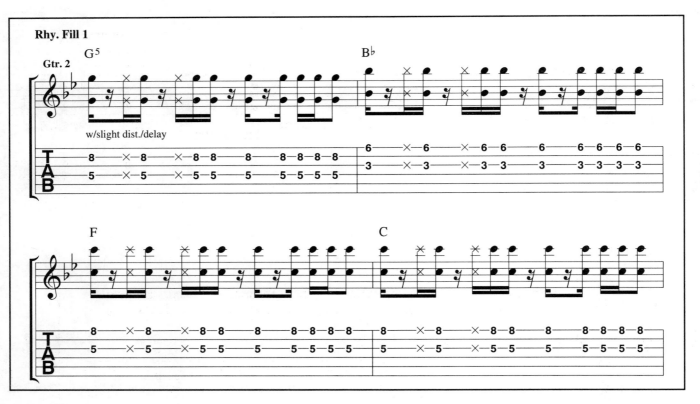

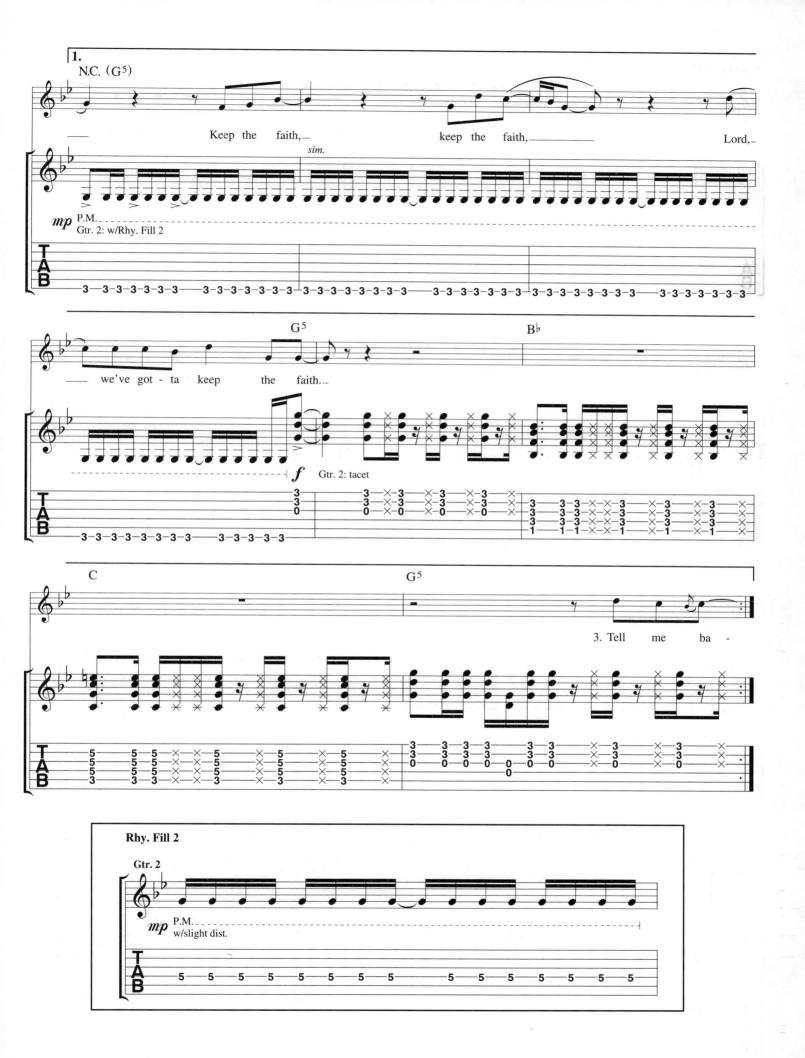

42

44

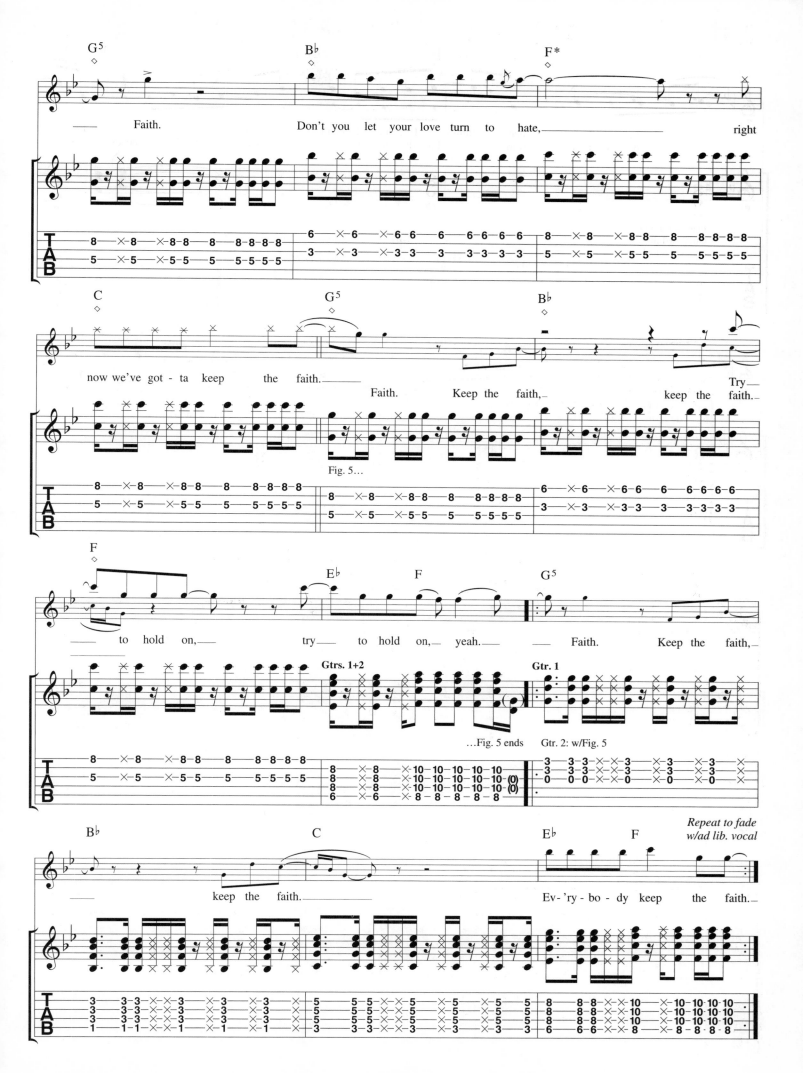

LOCAL BOY IN THE PHOTOGRAPH

Words & Music by Kelly Jones
Music by Richard Jones & Stuart Cable

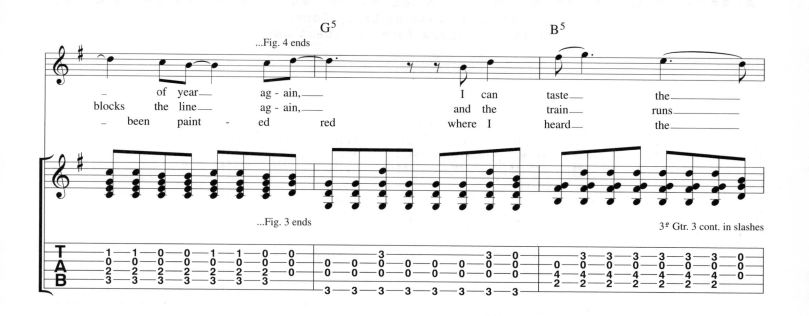

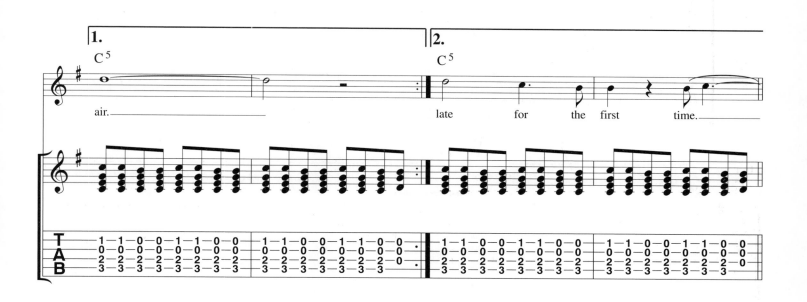

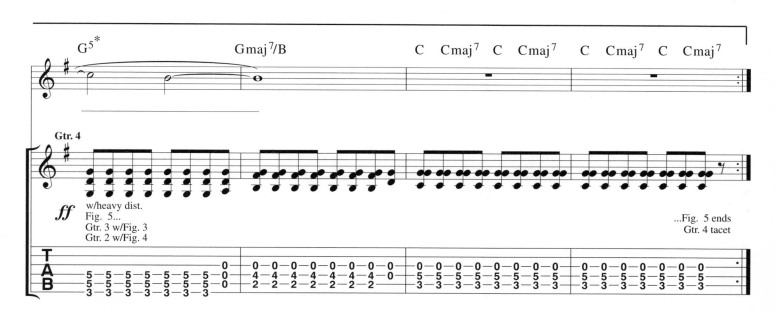

3.

C   Cmaj7   C   Cmaj7   C   Cmaj7   C   Cmaj7

Gtr. 2

news_____ for the first time._____

Gtr. 3

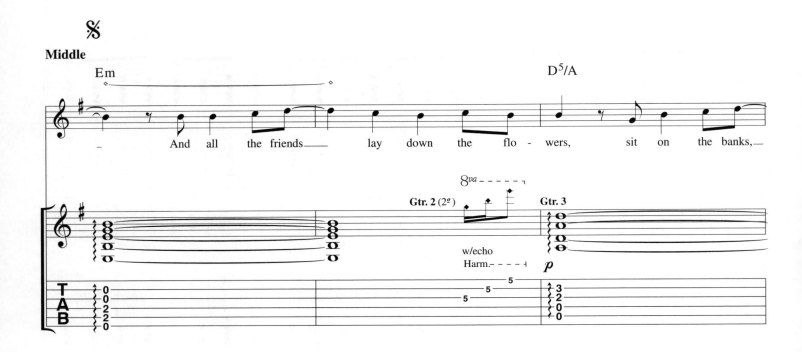

Middle

Em   D5/A

_ And all the friends____ lay down the flo - wers, sit on the banks,____

Gtr. 2 (2ª)   8va - - - - - -

Gtr. 3

w/echo
Harm.- - - - -   *p*

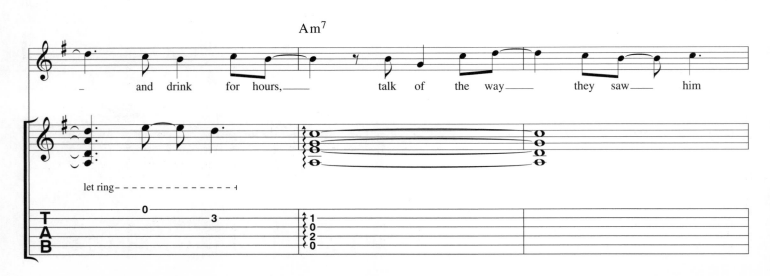

Am7

_ and drink for hours,____ talk of the way____ they saw____ him

let ring - - - - - - - - - - - -

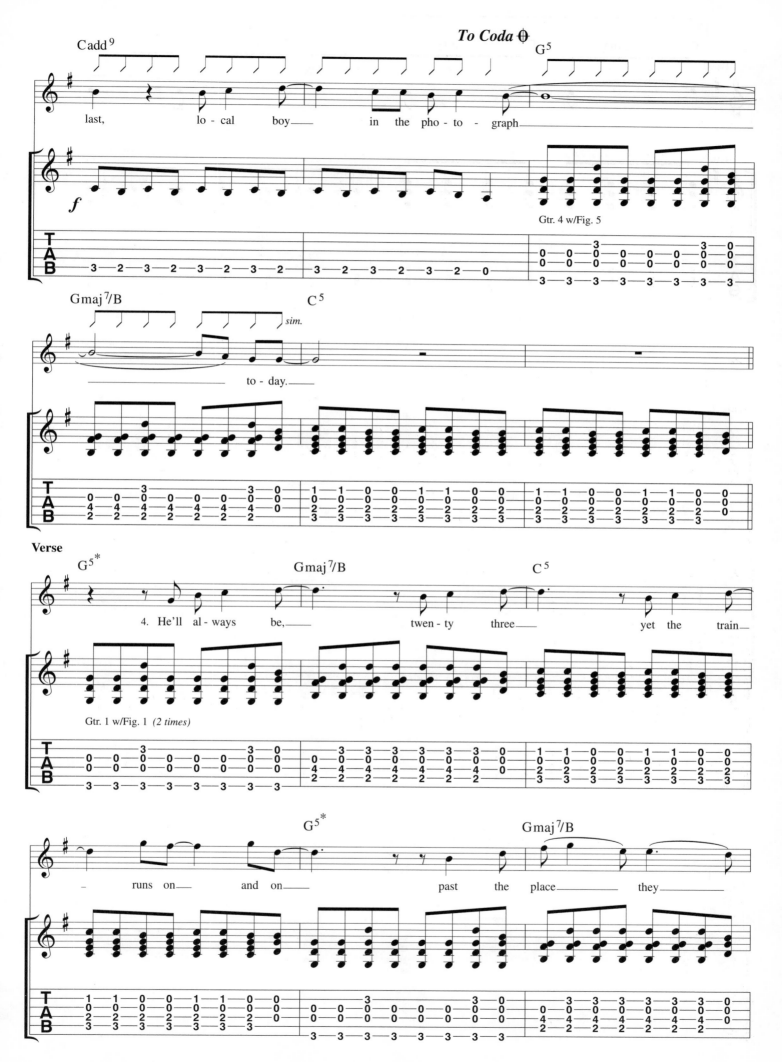

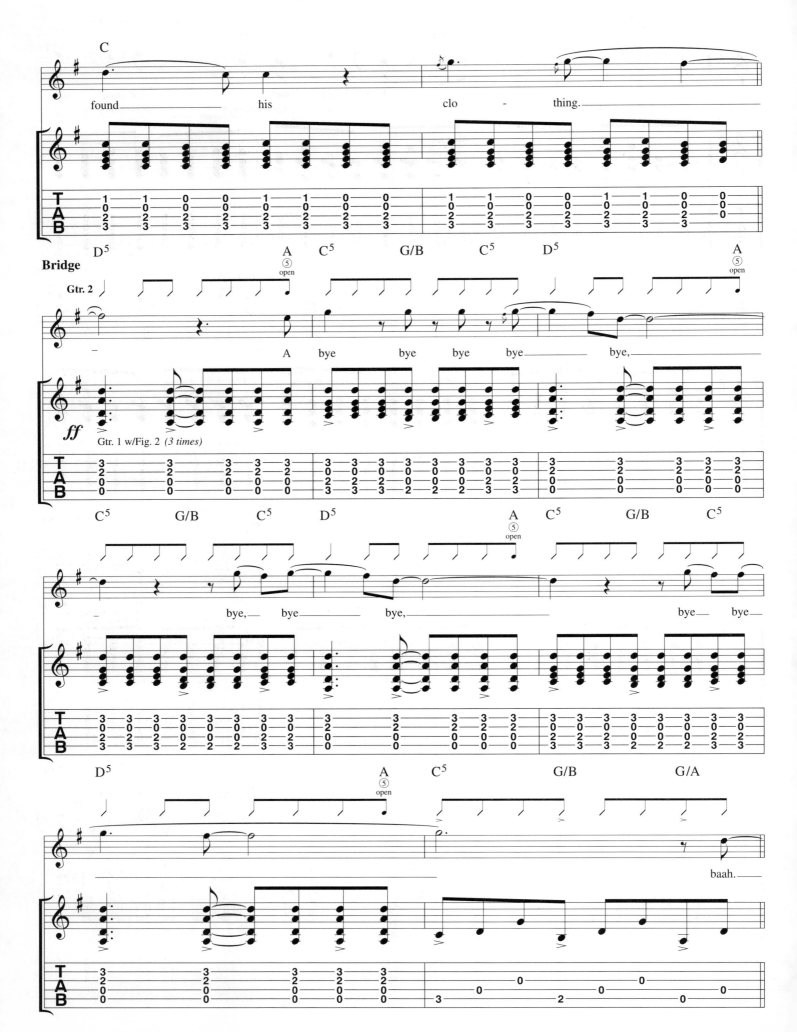

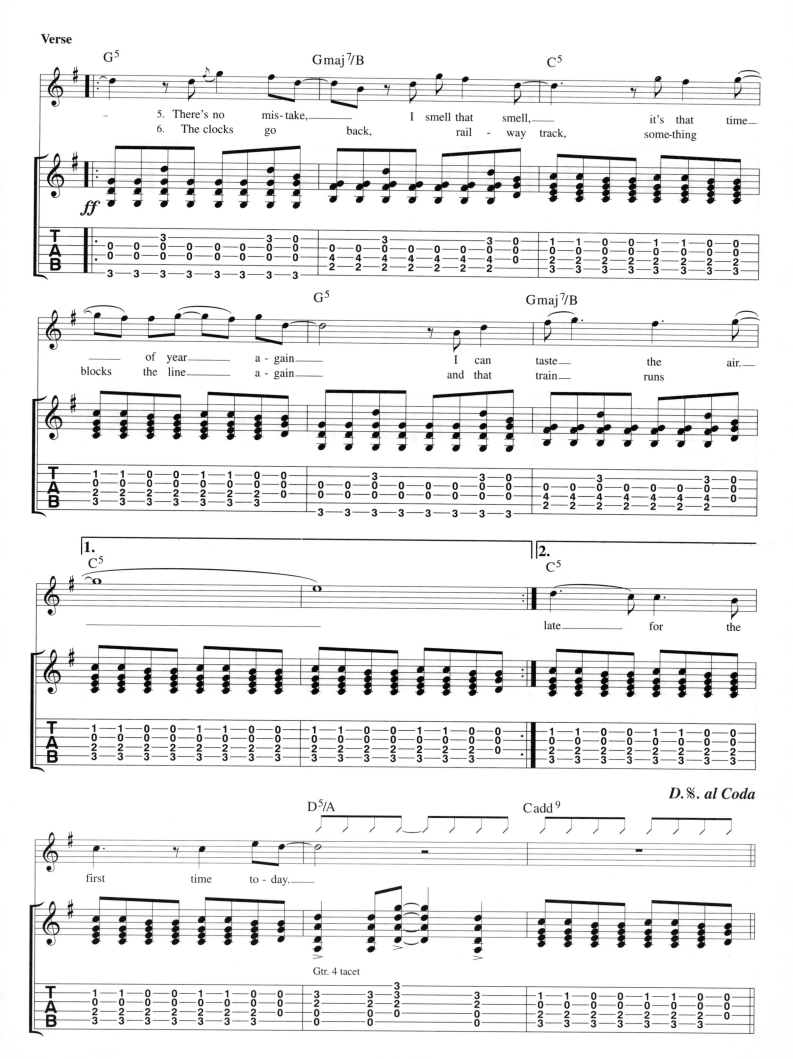

Verse

5. There's no mis-take,_____ I smell that smell,_____ it's that time_____
6. The clocks go back, rail - way track, some-thing

_____ of year_____ a - gain_____ I can taste the air._____
blocks the line_____ a - gain_____ and that train_____ runs

1. **2.**

late_____ for the

first time to - day._____

D.%. al Coda

Gtr. 4 tacet

51

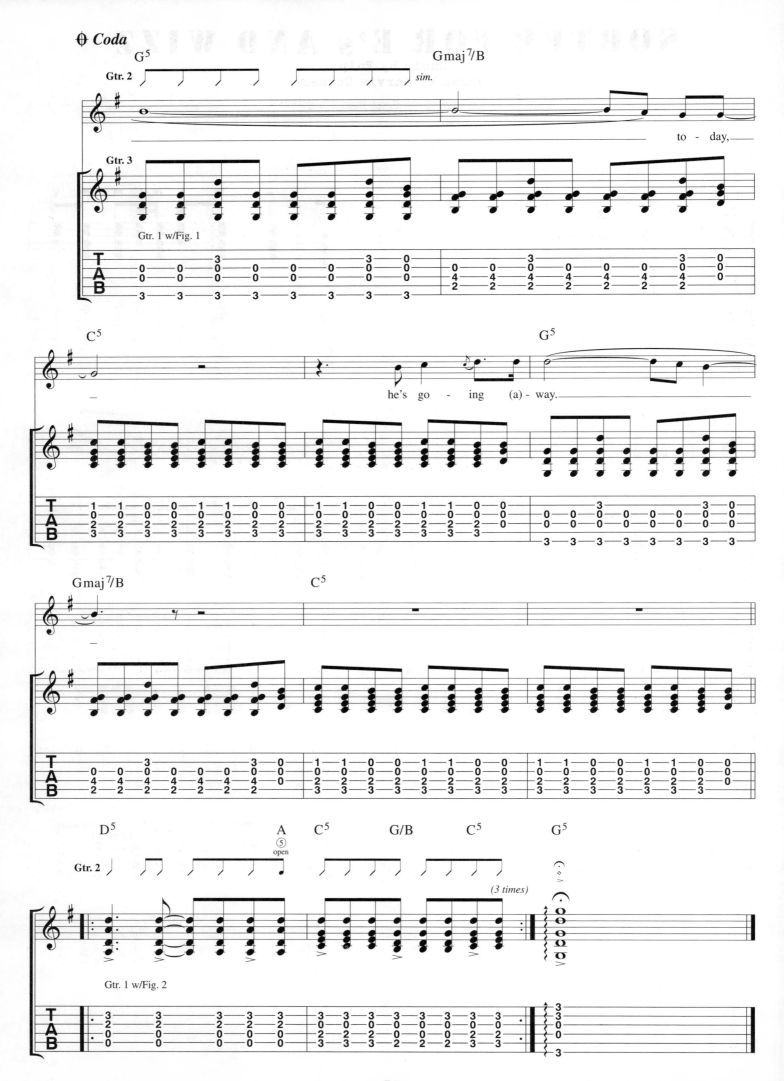

SORTED FOR E's AND WIZZ

Music by Pulp
Words by Jarvis Cocker

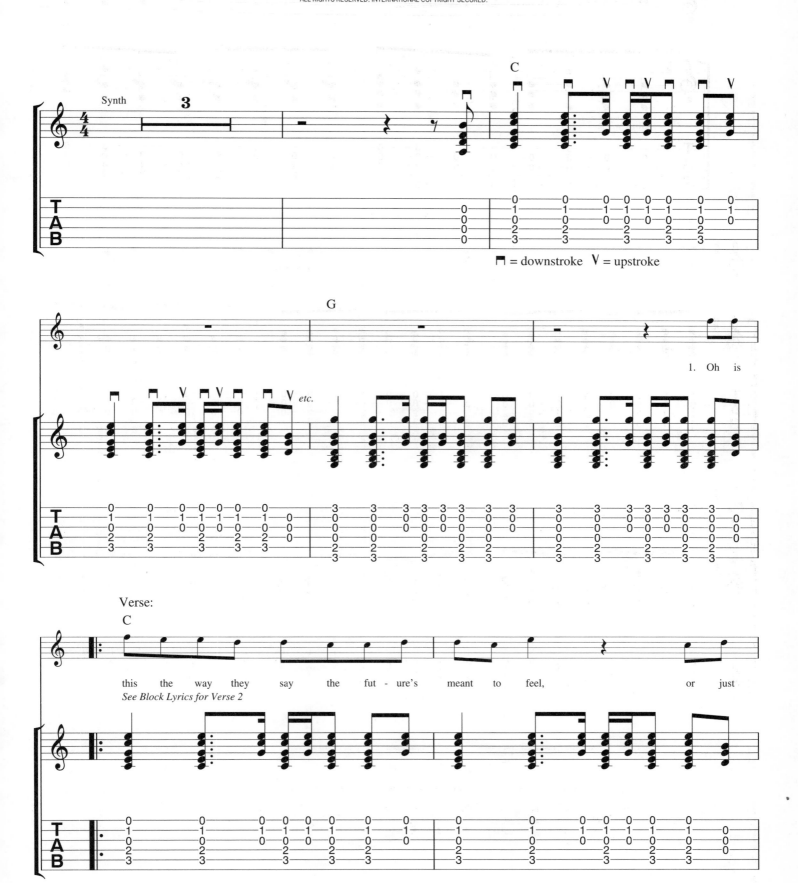

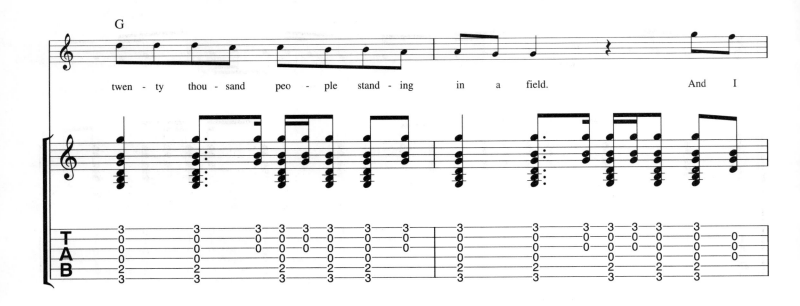

twen - ty thou - sand peo - ple stand - ing in a field. And I

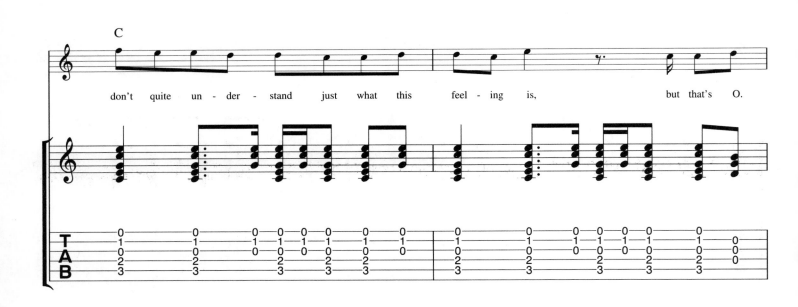

don't quite un - der - stand just what this feel - ing is, but that's O.

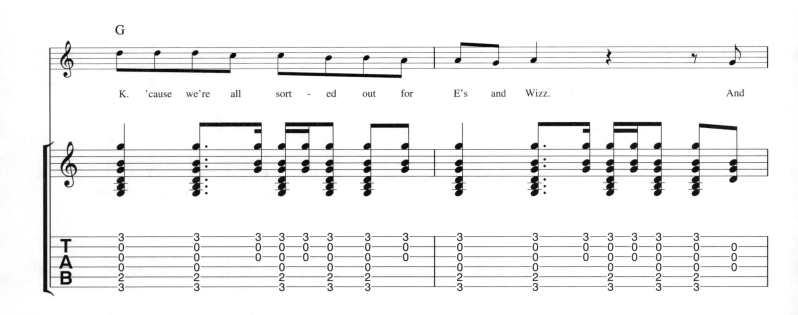

K. 'cause we're all sort - ed out for E's and Wizz. And

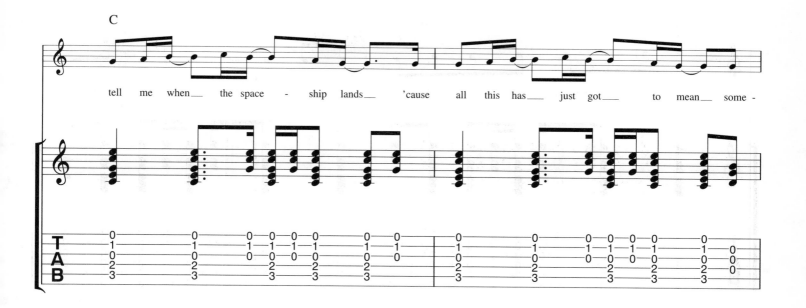

tell me when___ the space - ship lands___ 'cause all this has___ just got___ to mean___ some -

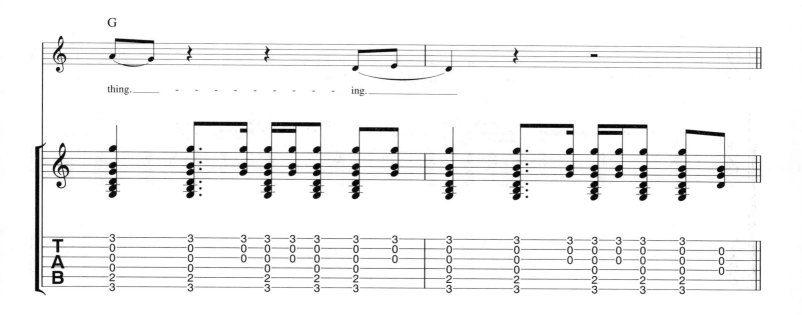

thing.___ - - - - - - - - ing.___

Chorus:

In the mid - dle of the night, it feels al - right but then to -

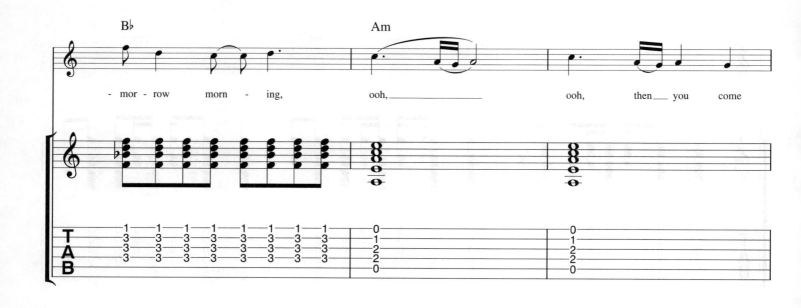

-mor - row morn - ing, ooh,_____ ooh, then___ you come

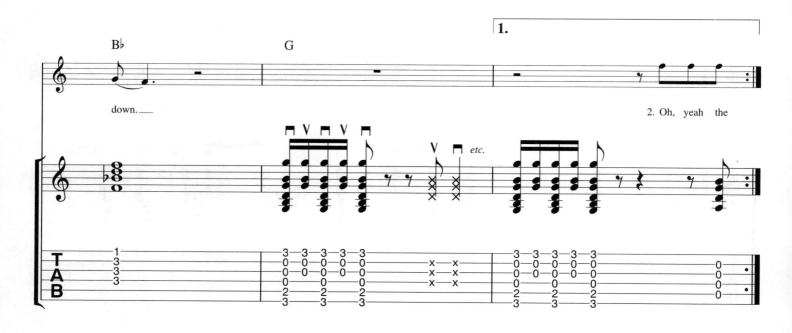

1.

down.___

2. Oh, yeah the

2.

Just keep on mov - ing.

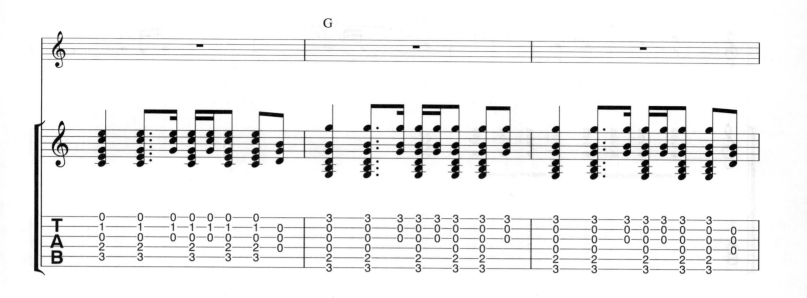

G

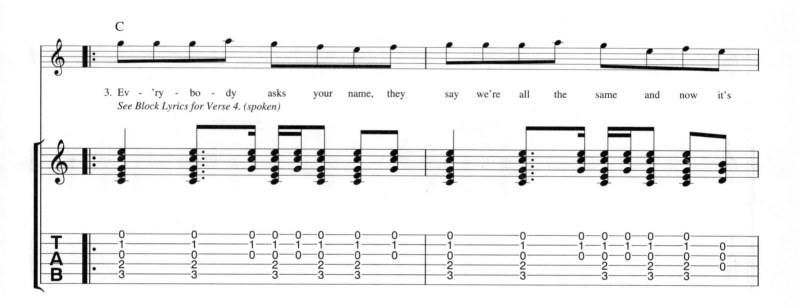

C

3. Ev - 'ry - bo - dy   asks   your   name,   they   say   we're   all   the   same   and   now   it's
See Block Lyrics for Verse 4. (spoken)

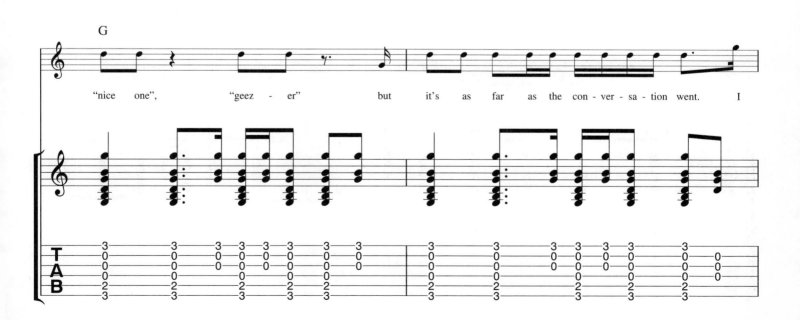

G

"nice   one",   "geez - er"   but   it's   as   far   as   the   con - ver - sa - tion   went.   I

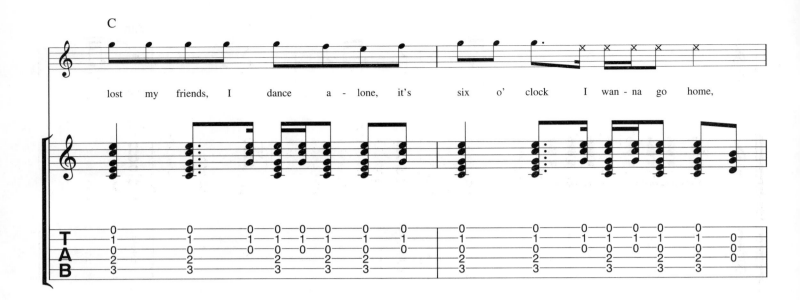

lost my friends, I dance a-lone, it's six o' clock I wan-na go home,

it's "no way"___ "not to-day"___ makes you won-der what it meant.___ (And this

Chorus:

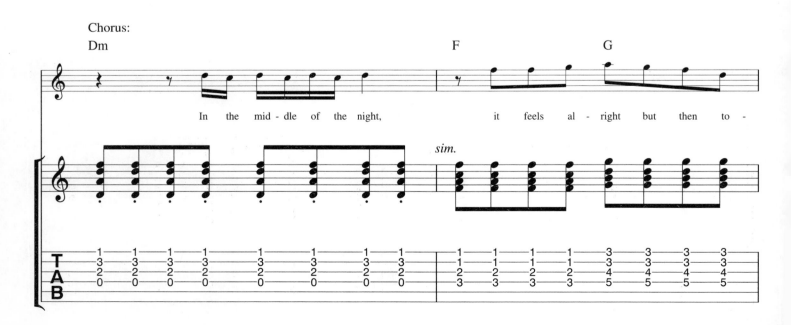

In the mid-dle of the night, it feels al-right but then to-

58

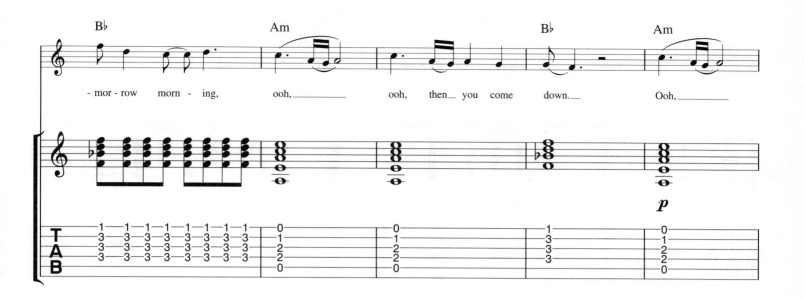

-mor - row morn - ing, ooh, _____ ooh, then_ you come down._ Ooh, _____

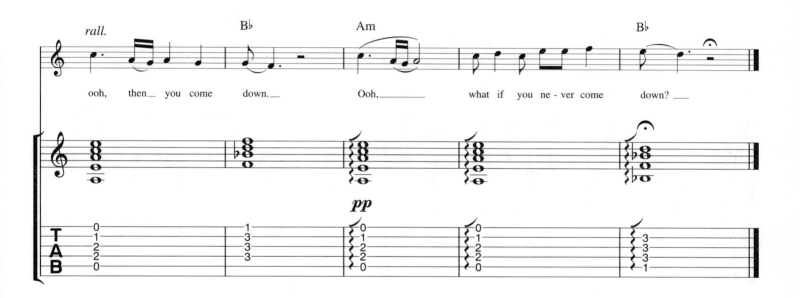

ooh, then_ you come down._ Ooh, _____ what if you ne - ver come down? _

TEN STOREY LOVE SONG

Words & Music by John Squire

THE CHANGINGMAN
Words & Music by Paul Weller & Brendan Lynch

68

THE RIVERBOAT SONG

**Words & Music by Simon Fowler, Steve Cradock,
Oscar Harrison & Damon Minchella**

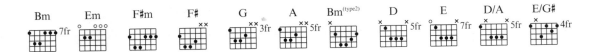

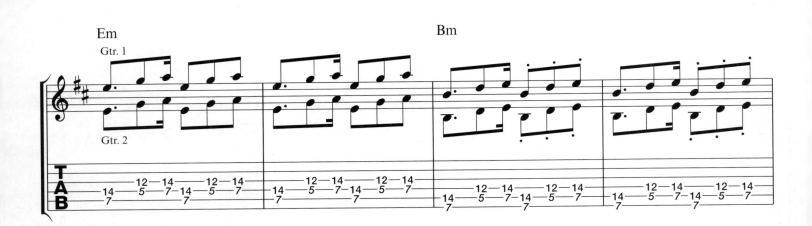

I see

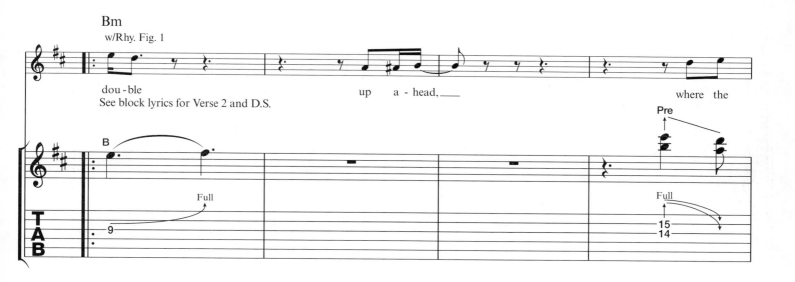

dou-ble

See block lyrics for Verse 2 and D.S.

up a-head,___

where the

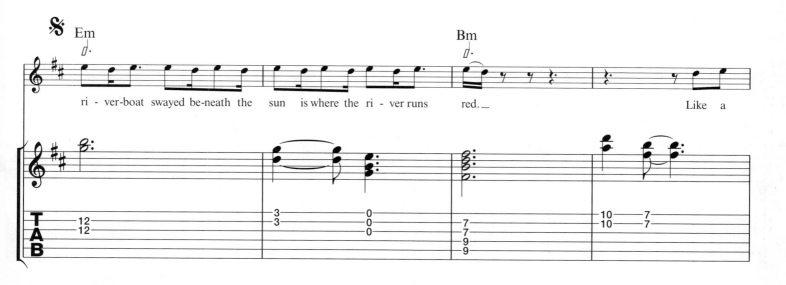

ri-ver-boat swayed be-neath the sun is where the ri-ver runs red.___

Like a

king who stalks the wings and shoots a dove and frees an ea - gle in - stead. It's

more or less the same as the things___ that you said.

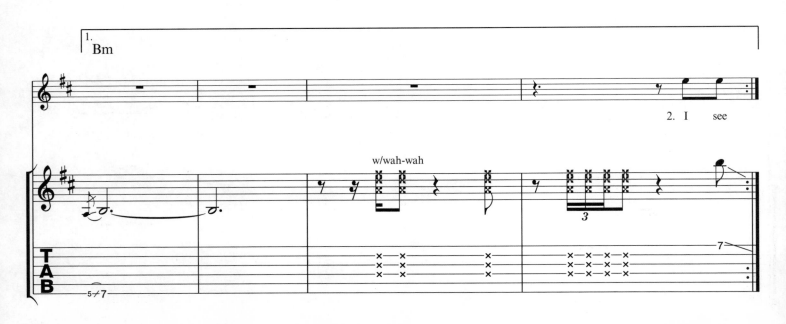

2. I see

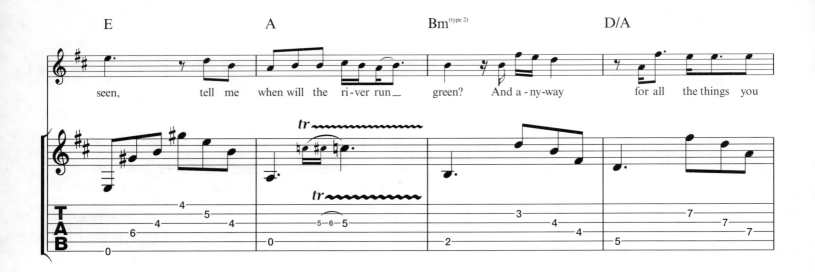

seen,   tell me   when will the   ri-ver run__   green?   And a-ny-way   for all   the things   you

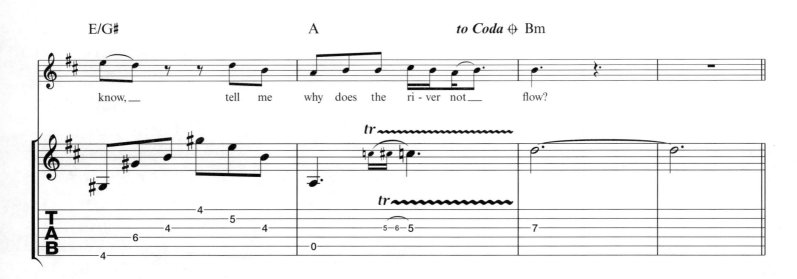

know,__   tell me   why does the   ri-ver not__   flow?

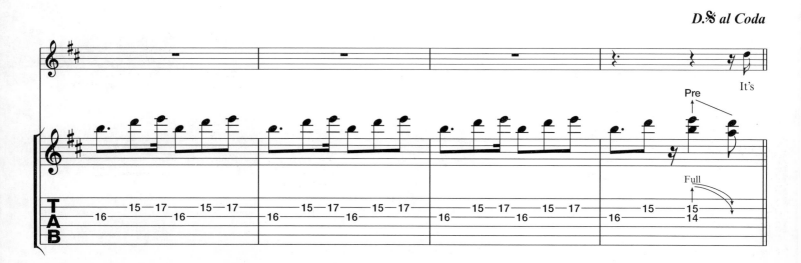

D.% al Coda

Pre

It's

Full

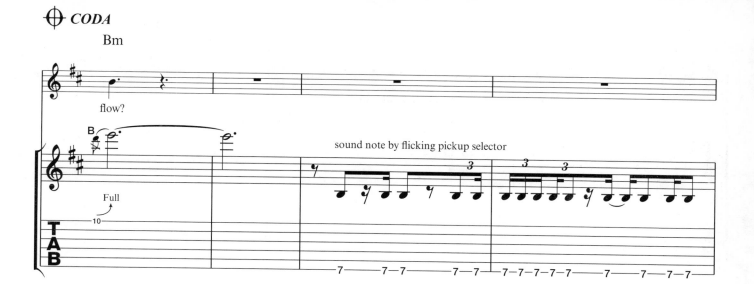

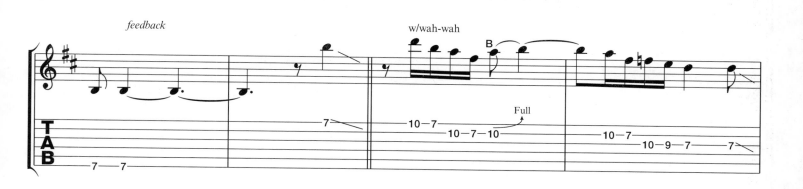

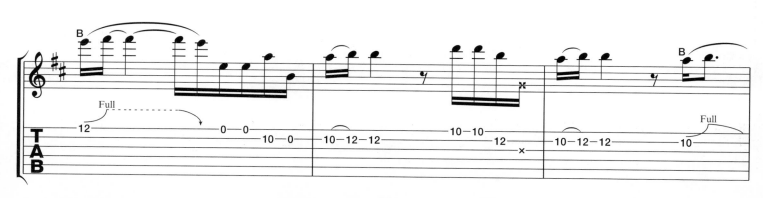

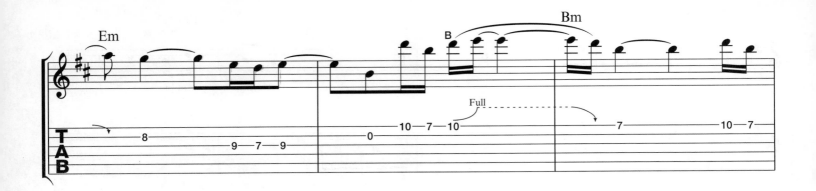

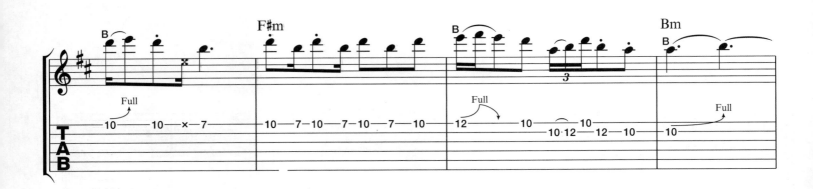

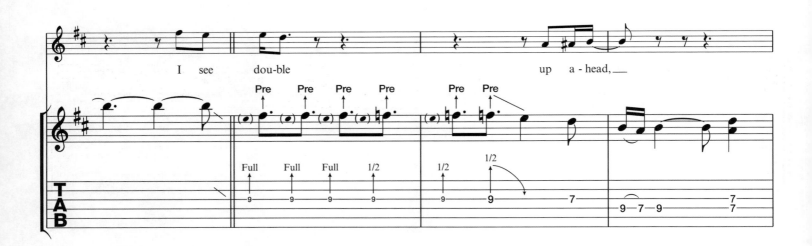

I see   dou-ble   up   a-head,__

where the   riv - er-boat swayed be-neath the   sun   is where the riv - er runs__   red.

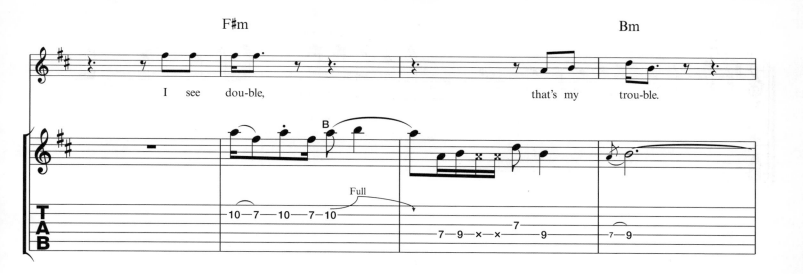

I see dou-ble, that's my trou-ble.

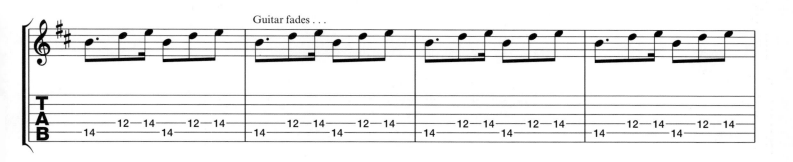

Guitar fades . . .

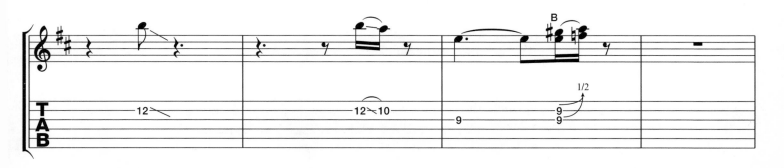

77

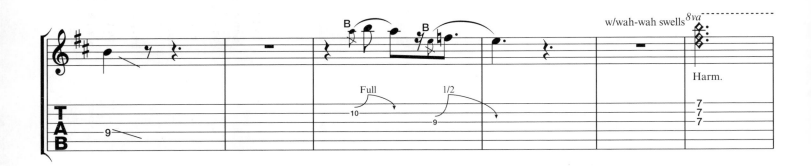

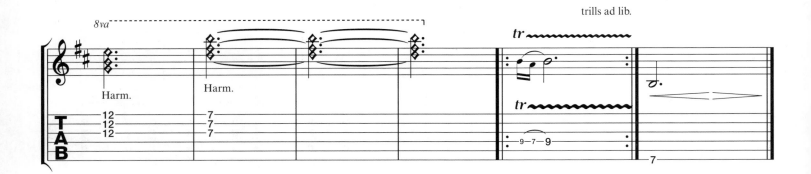

Verse 2

I see trouble up the road
Like the things you found in love are by the way
And like to cheat on your soul
Like the best and worst of thoughts that lose control
Before you lie on your bed
It's more or less the same as the things that you said

D.%.

It's more or less the things
You fail to say in your way that's your trouble
Like a king who stalks the wings
And shoots the moon and the stars
And his double
It's more or less the same as the things that you said

I see double up ahead
Where the riverboat swayed beneath the sun
Is where the river runs red
I see double – that's my trouble

ZOMBIE

Words & Music by Dolores O'Riordan

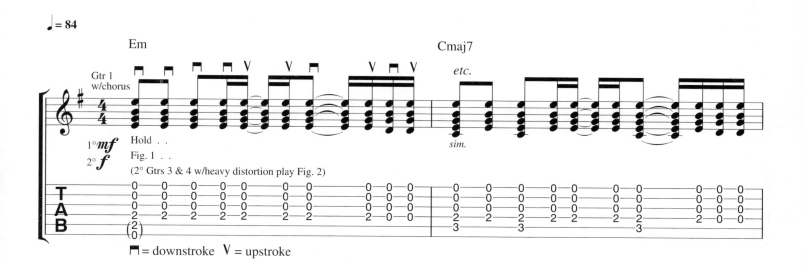

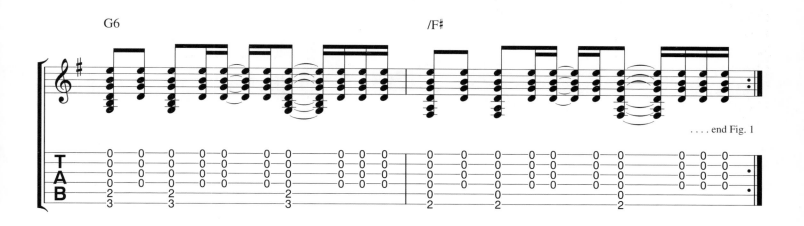

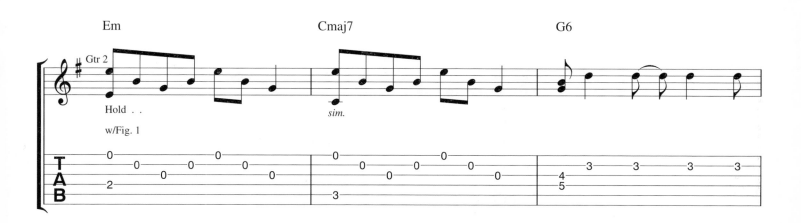

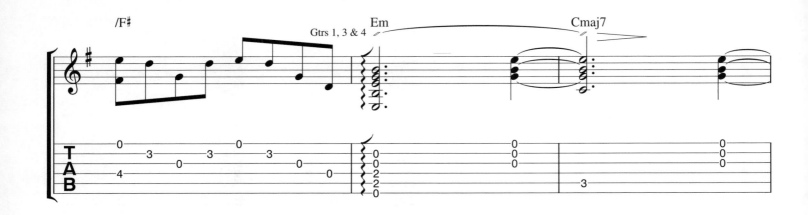

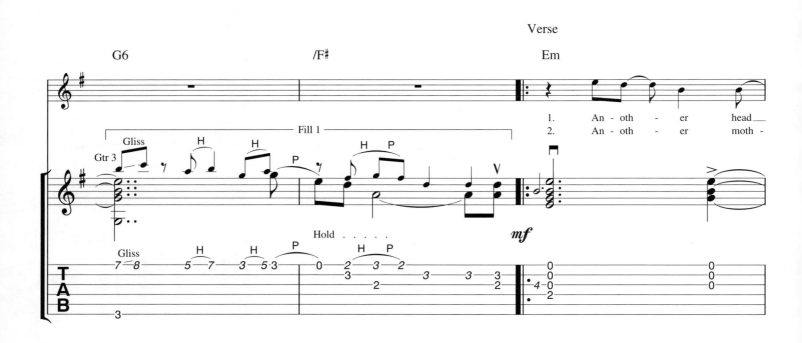

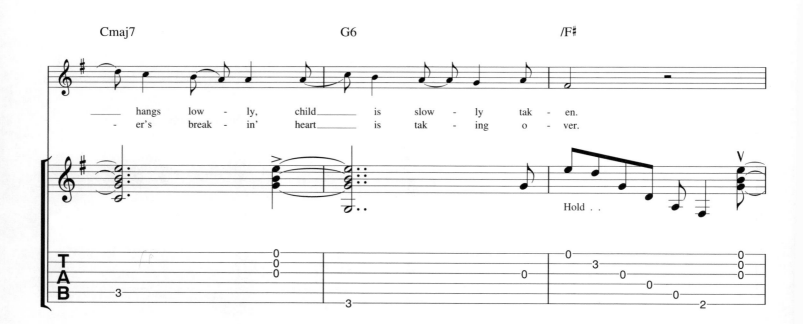

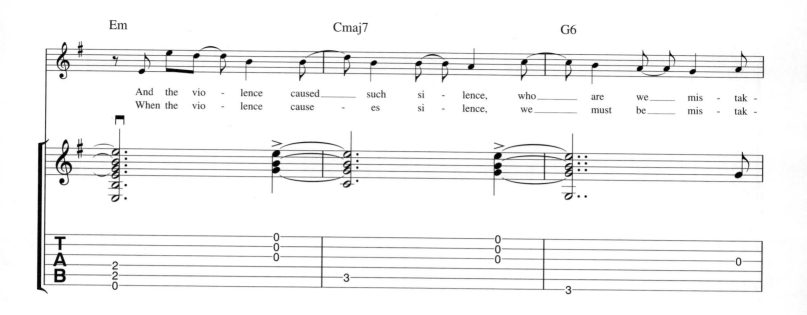

And the vio - lence caused____ such si - lence, who____ are we____ mis - tak -
When the vio - lence cause - es si - lence, we____ must be____ mis - tak -

- en? But you see, it's not me, it's not my fam - i - ly, in your head,__
- en. It's the same old____ theme since____ nine - teen six - teen, in your head,__

____ in your head they are fight - ing._____ With their tanks and their bombs and their bombs
____ in your head they're still fight - ing._____ With their tanks and their bombs and their bombs

Hold . . . . ┘

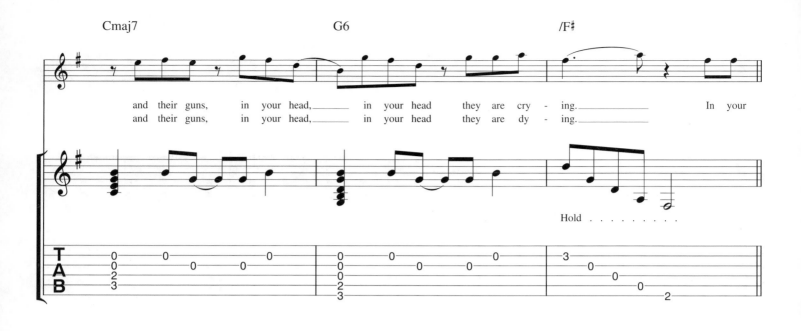

Cmaj7   G6   /F♯

and their guns, in your head,_____ in your head they are cry - ing._____ In your
and their guns, in your head,_____ in your head they are dy - ing._____

Hold . . . .

Chorus

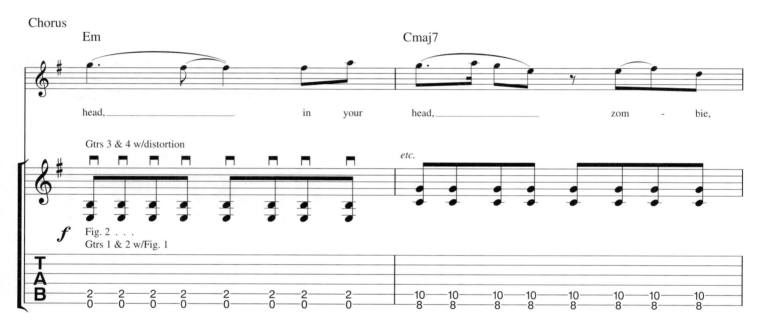

Em   Cmaj7

head,_____ in your head,_____ zom - bie,

Gtrs 3 & 4 w/distortion

etc.

f Fig. 2 . . .
Gtrs 1 & 2 w/Fig. 1

G6   /F♯

zom - bie, zom - bie, hey,_____ hey. What's in your

. . . . end Fig. 2

82

head,_____ in your head,_____ zom - bie,

zom - bie, zom - bie, hey,_____ hey,_____ hey._____ Oh_____

1.

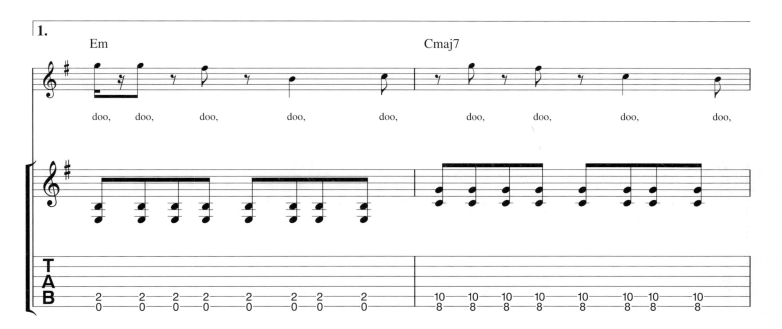

doo, doo, doo, doo, doo, doo, doo, doo, doo,

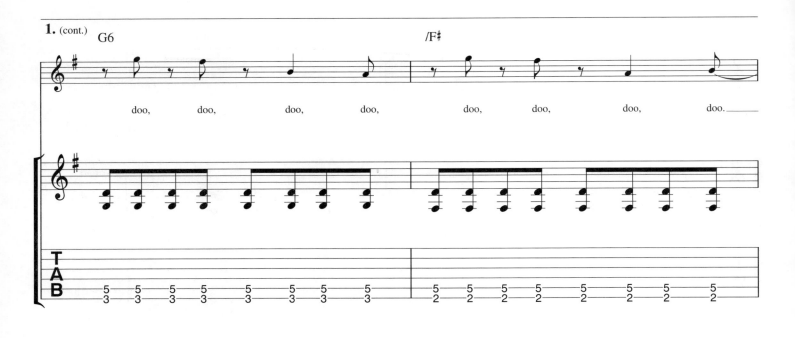

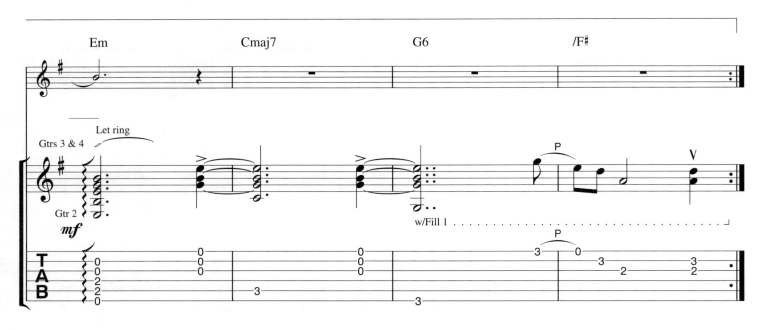

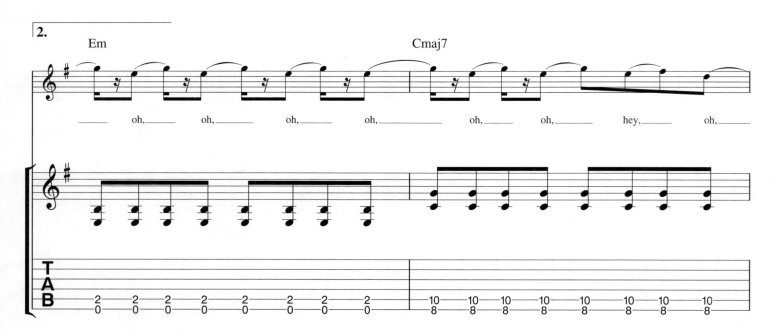

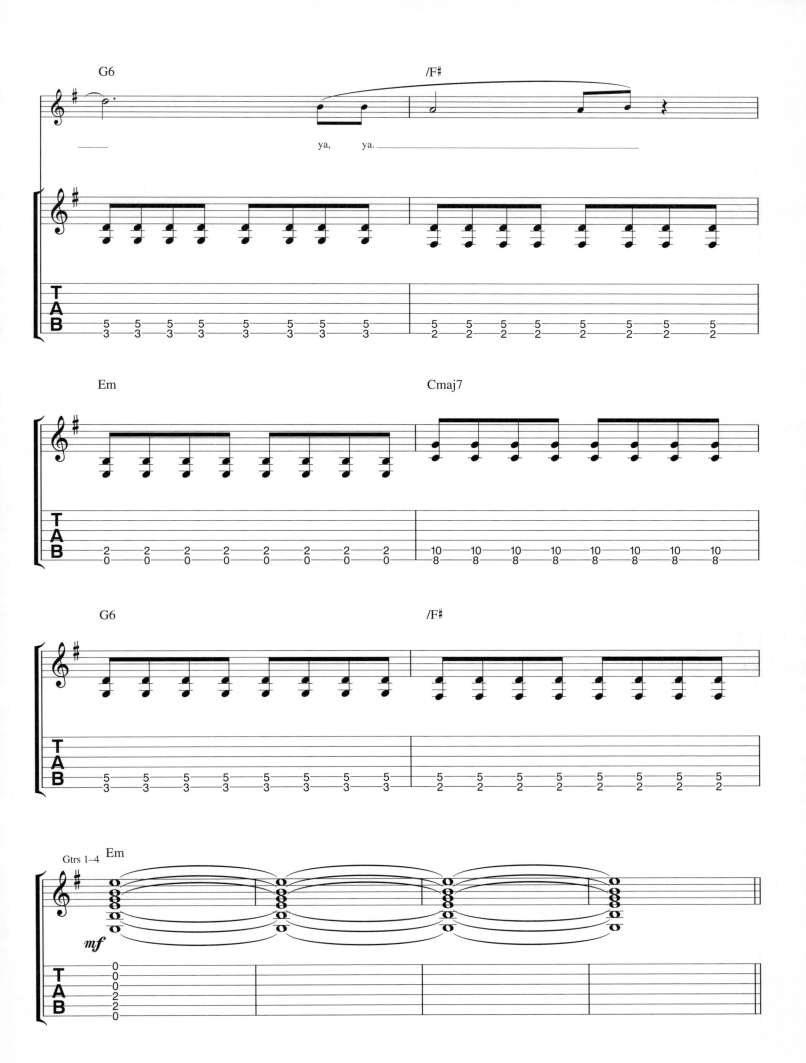

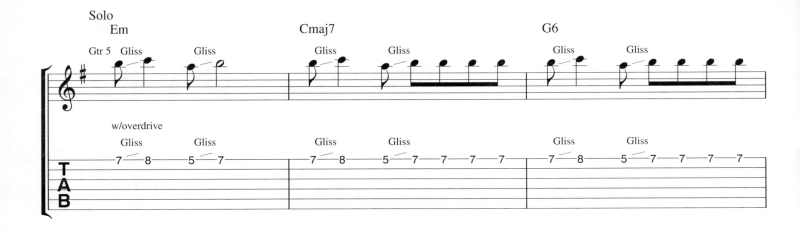

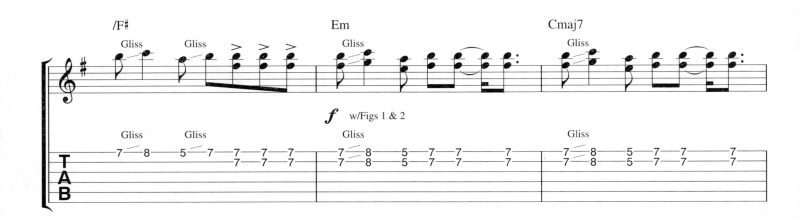

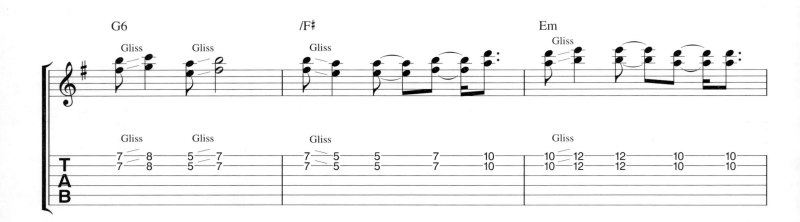

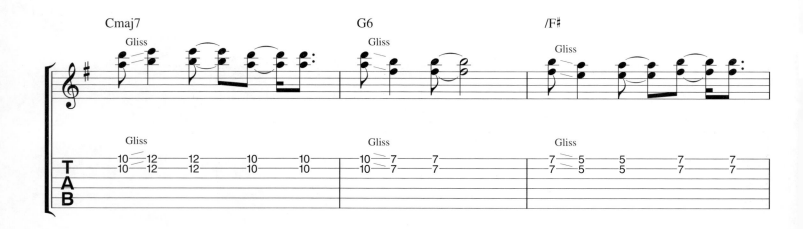

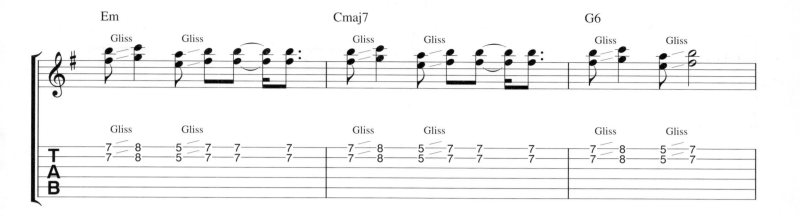

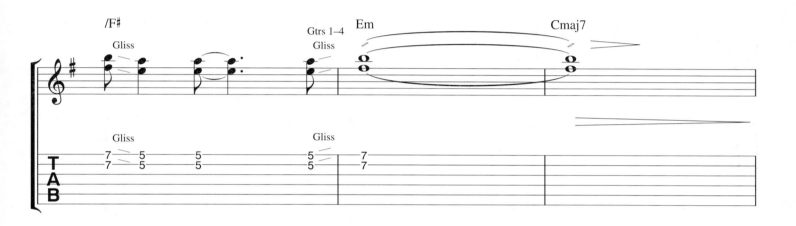

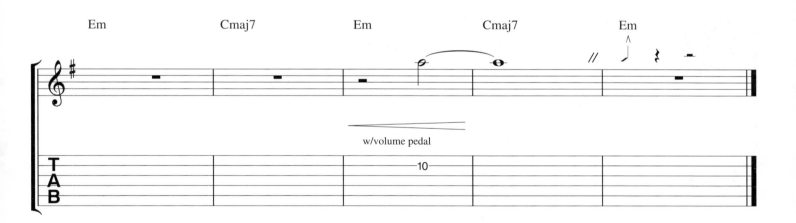

WIDE OPEN SPACE

Words & Music by Paul Draper

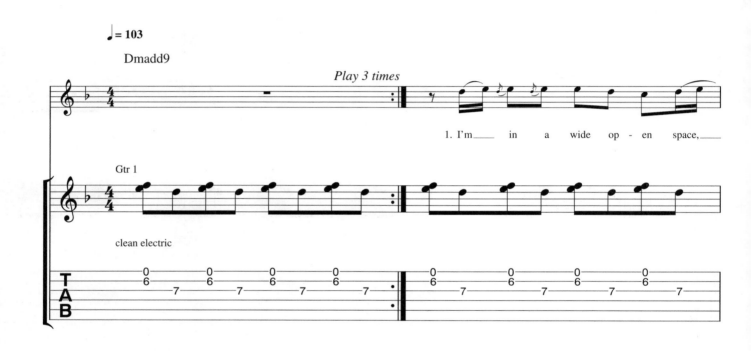

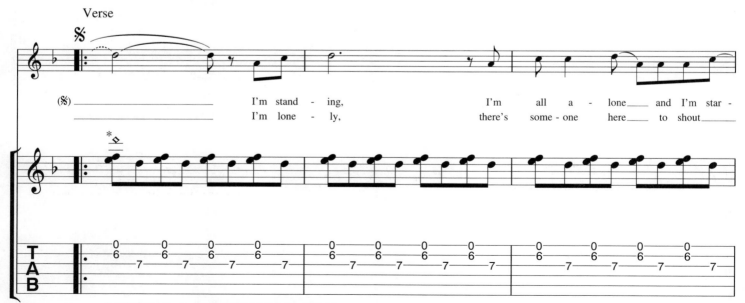

* end of solo, harmonic played at 3 1/3 fret on 3rd string

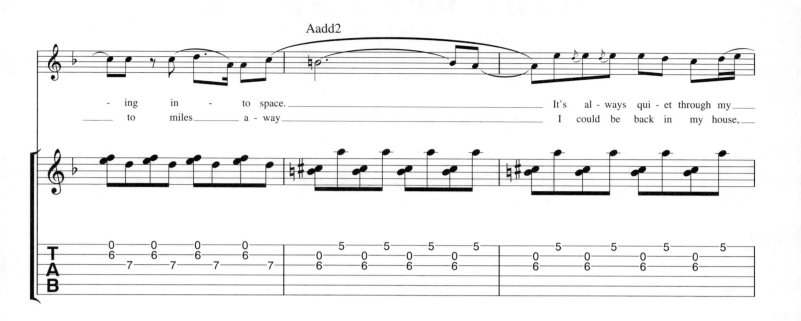

- ing in - to space._____ It's al - ways qui - et through my_____
_____ to miles_____ a - way_____ I could be back in my house,

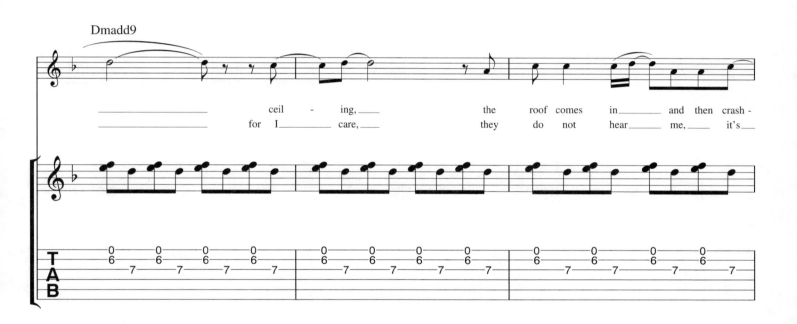

_____ ceil - ing,_____ the roof comes in_____ and then crash -
_____ for I_____ care, they do not hear_____ me,____ it's

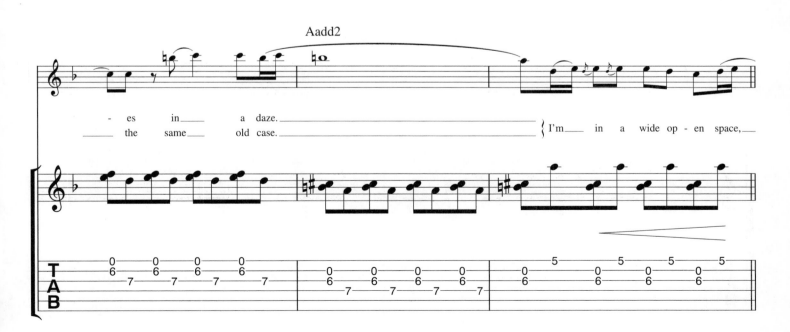

- es in_____ a daze._____
_____ the same_____ old case._____ I'm__ in a wide op - en space,_____

Chorus

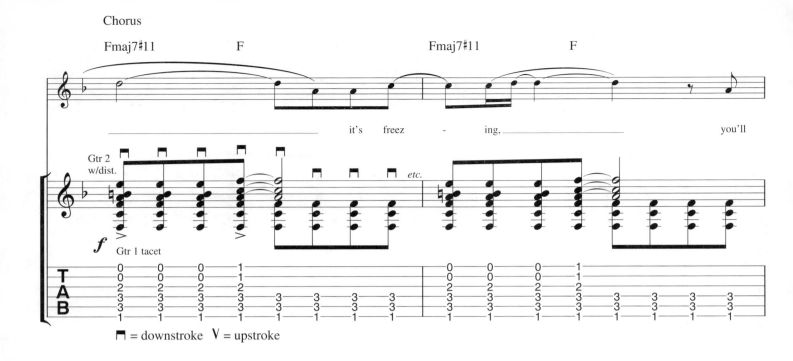

it's freez - ing, _____ you'll

= downstroke   V = upstroke

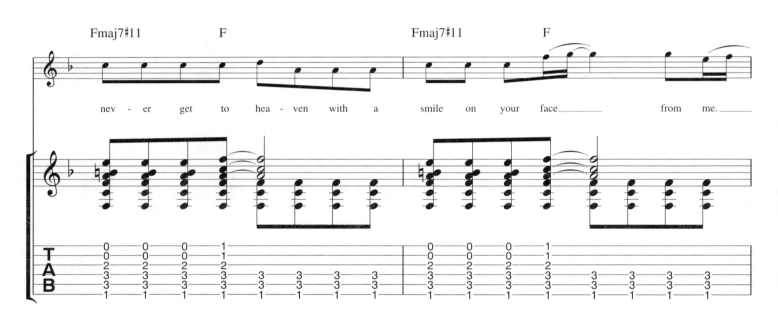

nev - er get to hea - ven with a smile on your face_____ from me. _____

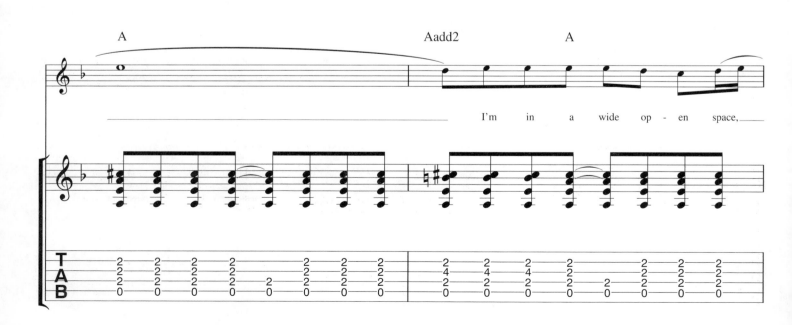

I'm in a wide op - en space, _____

I'm star - ing, _____ there's

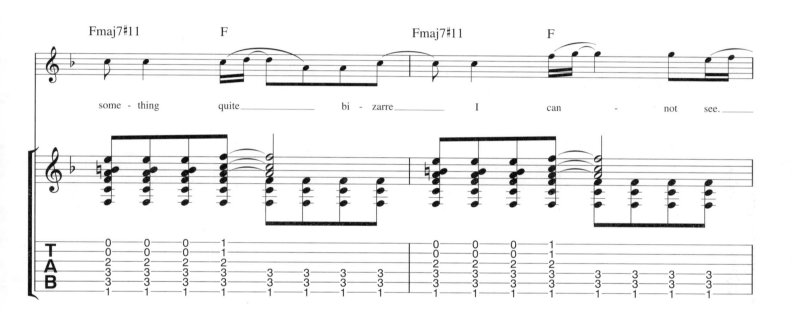

some - thing quite___ bi - zarre ___ I can - not see. ___

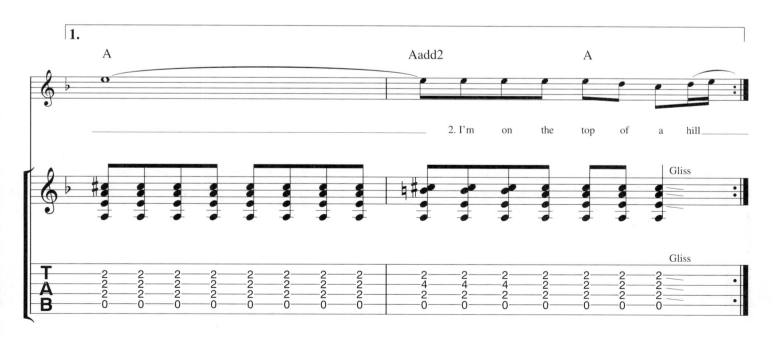

1.

2. I'm on the top of a hill ___

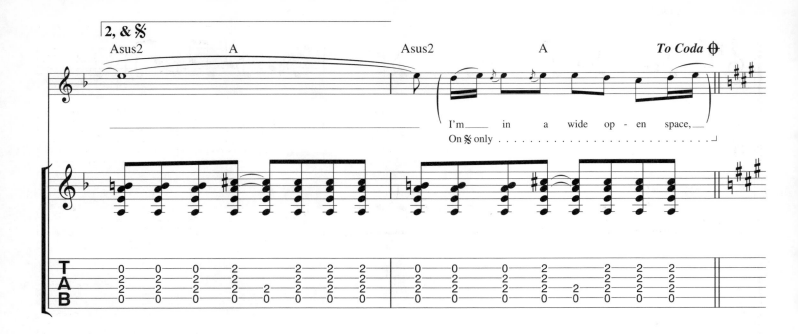

Solo

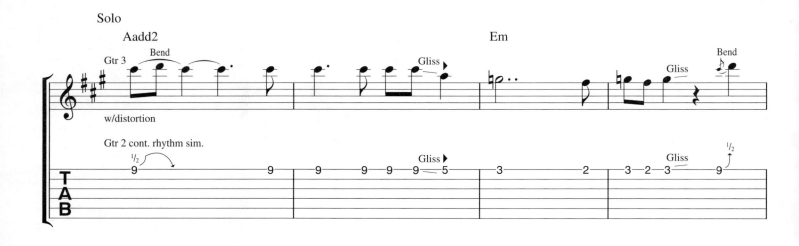

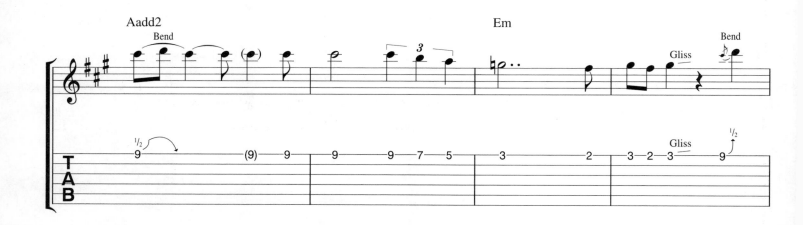

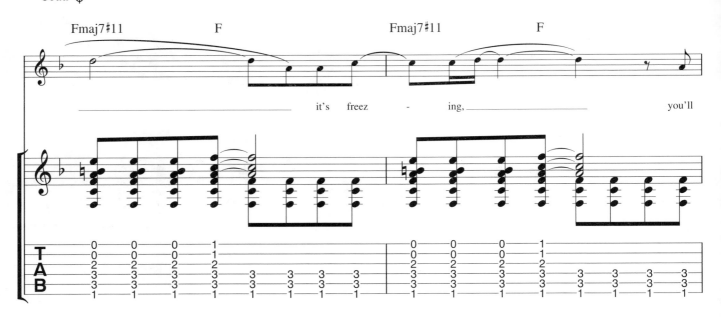

it's freez - ing, _____ you'll

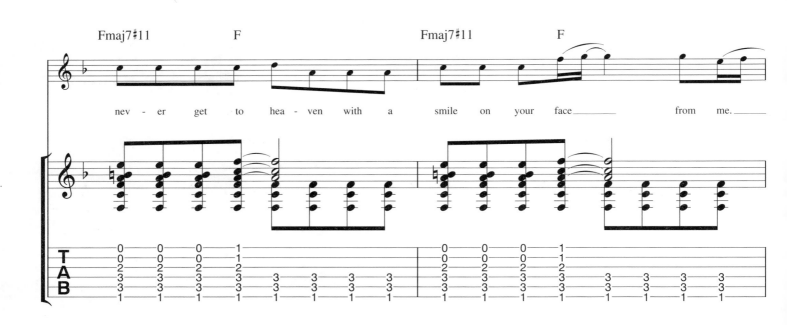

nev - er get to hea - ven with a smile on your face _____ from me. _____

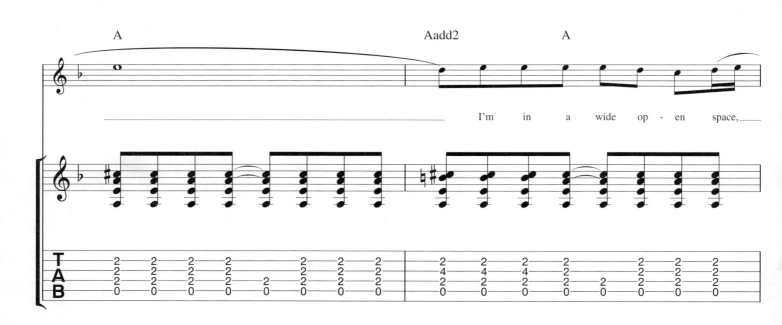

I'm in a wide op - en space, _____

I'm star - ing, there's

some - thing quite bi - zarre I can not see.

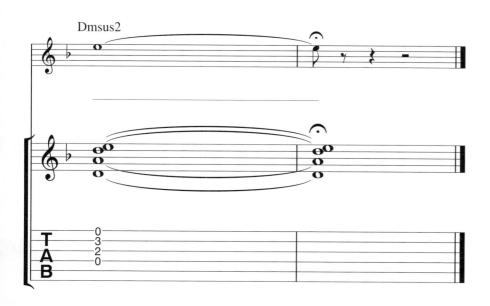